EGO & MILIEU

EGC

& MILIEU

Theory and Practice of Environmental Therapy

JOHN CUMMING
ELAINE CUMMING

FOREWORD BY ALFRED H. STANTON

ALDINE·ATHERTON/CHICAGO AND NEW YORK

EGO & MILIEU: THEORY AND PRACTICE
OF ENVIRONMENTAL THERAPY
by John Cumming and Elaine Cumming

Copyright © 1962 by Atherton Press

Copyright under International, Pan American,
and Universal Copyright Conventions

Library of Congress Catalogue Card Number: 62–18829

Printed in the United States of America

Designed by Polly Cameron

Eighth Printing 1972

Foreword
by Alfred H. Stanton, M.D.

Ego and Milieu is a straightforward attack upon perhaps the critically central problem of contemporary psychiatry— the analysis of the relation between the hospital and treatment environment and the character of psychiatric illness. Recent years have brought much reason to believe that the onset, symptoms, and recovery rates of major psychiatric illness are decisively influenced by the environment within which the patient is observed and treated; with this belief has come the recognition that more definitive scientific analysis of these disorders will require a much more sophisticated understanding of this relationship than is now available to us. Since this understanding is important both from a practical clinical standpoint and as a base for the analysis of all research in the major psychiatric disorders, its pursuit belongs in the very first priority in the psychiatric research program. There is no patient "untreated" by his environment—only patients "treated," well or ill.

Reasons for the inadequacy of our grasp of the nature of

the interaction between the hospital and treatment environment, the patient and his psychiatric disorder are not hard to find. The overwhelming service demands placed upon psychiatrists and the other professionals associated with the psychiatric effort cannot help but favor a desperate grasping at any device which promises some relief for a few patients. Competition for the services of the professionals best educated for scientific analysis is very high, drawing them away from theoretical and research careers and separating clinical gifts and experience from systematic analytic abilities. Perhaps more important, any procedure which promises and delivers some help is treated at a technical level—on the basis of how to do it—rather than also at the theoretical level—what does it do, how does it affect change? The reforms in psychiatric hospital practices since World War II have been heavily influenced by this trend.

This has not been from lack of effort by workers in the field to make their work scientifically and theoretically pertinent. Social and behavioral scientists have been prominent in many recent studies and have brought with them both theoretical and empirical abilities which have been put to use in a respectable series of studies but leaving much to be done. Psychoanalytic theory suggested an expectation that the environment would prove to be of critical importance and led to many of the early studies of the therapeutic milieu, although usually in a form which did not lead to specific testing either of psychoanalytic theoretical concepts or of the milieu practices reputedly derived from them. The British drew heavily upon the formulations of the Kurt Lewin group both theoretically and for empirical procedures of investigation together, often, with a psychoanalytic orientation. Again the outcomes seem to be less related to the principles of Lewinian psychology than earlier judgments would lead one to expect. Harry Stack Sullivan's interpersonal theories led less to the study of the psychiatric

hospital as a therapeutic instrument than did his earlier practices and clinical insights. The result has been the development of a body of information as "clinical" as a description of
a sick person, full of suggestive statements, obviously deeply
pertinent to the clinical problems of practitioners, but with
each study standing largely upon its own without there arising
a body of cumulative knowledge and of deepening analytic
implications which the field promises. Much is known about
how empirical study and observation should be carried out,
and much more is being worked out—but the theoretical integration has failed to appear. We are like Withering with digi-
talis—*in possession of an obviously effective and dangerous
therapeutic agent whose mode of action is complex and hardly
understood at all beyond the empiric recognition that it works.*

The Cummings bring to this situation the backgrounds of
a psychiatrist and of a sociologist, both with long experience in
clinical situations. This combination has contributed to making
this study a major contribution in developing this theoretical
integration. John Cumming has worked as a psychiatrist in a
large provincial hospital, a small receiving hospital, a veterans
hospital, and, for shorter periods, in other clinical institutions.
Elaine Cumming has shared much of this experience from the
point of view of a sociologist and has contributed with her
husband in the systematic analysis of milieu function. Both
have studied community aspects of the mental health field. But
more important for our present purposes, their practical familiarity with the clinical situation is matched by a long research
experience and theoretical abilities and interests, which have
led to a number of incisive analytic studies of therapeutic institutions which do point toward the development of a more
sophisticated level of knowledge. Using a point of view derived
largely from the sociological theories of Talcott Parsons and the
psychological theories of Erik Erikson, the Cummings have con-
fronted directly the fact that an understanding of the action

of any therapeutic agent requires knowledge of how the agent articulates with the illness. This is a more important effort than may appear at first glance. Conceptually unsolved issues in the relation of environmental and interpersonal situations to subjective, intrapersonal, mental phenomena are reminiscent of the problems in the mind-body dichotomy and, as in the older philosophical problem, logical and empirical problems remain unsettled and not even satisfactorily disentangled today. If psychiatric writers have usually tended to think of illness as within the person and social scientists (including Sullivan the psychiatrist) have tended to think of the person as suffering difficulty in interpersonal relations, the outcome has been that the critical importance of any bridging concepts, both theoretically for a psychology of personality and practically for a theory of therapy, has often been overshadowed by a noncritical contentiousness characteristic of different schools of thought.

In contrast, the Cummings offer certain of these bridging concepts and their empirical correlates, and bring the area closer to more critical research than has been within reach. The number of pertinent variables is doubtless large but is far short of infinite, and their considerations give ground for focusing our efforts and attention to a considerable degree.

If this area of research is not an easy one, if the basic methods of research are still being worked out and are not agreed upon, it is nevertheless true that information can be gained in the field, and it will be easier to do it now with this book before us. Rather than giving a clarion call to action of a predetermined sort, John and Elaine Cumming offer genuine help toward taking—and understanding—a more effective action.

ALFRED H. STANTON, M.D.
Psychiatrist in Chief, McLean Hospital
Associate Professor of Psychiatry, Harvard Medical School

Preface

We have written a theoretical book about our practical experience in hospitals, clinics, and community. Our clinical and intellectual indebtedness to those with whom we have planned, worked, and argued are reflected in references throughout the book and in the Introduction to Part II.

Many of the nurses and attendants whose daily rounds of work can be glimpsed between the lines of these pages are not mentioned, yet we owe much to them. We are particularly grateful to ward supervisors Jack McIlmoyl, Casper Lix, George Moore, Albert Atkinson, and Alvin Blakely of Weyburn Hospital who pooled their practical knowledge with our theory in a working partnership. We would like to thank Jerold Ingram for taking careful notes at ward meetings throughout our two years at the Kansas City Receiving Center. Many excerpts are quoted here.

To the Medical Superintendents, here and abroad, who spent valuable time showing us their hospitals, we are grateful, for we learned something from each.

Our present colleagues at the Syracuse Mental Health Research Unit have made major contributions to this book in seminars, discussion, and the preparation of materials. Robert J. Turner, in particular, gave us the benefit of his intense interest in the theories of Erik Erikson, Paul Federn, and Robert White. We owe special gratitude to Irwin Goffman for communicating to us some of the subtlety of his own thinking. Frances Durgin and Abraham Halpern read parts of the manuscript and made useful suggestions. Rhondda Cassetta read and checked the manuscript, supervised its production, read the proof, and acted as an editorial advisor; we thank her warmly.

The typing of the manuscript was most ably supervised by Agnes Helliwell. For permission to paraphrase and to quote excerpts we thank the following: *The Digest of Neurology and Psychiatry,* Harvard University Press, *Psychiatry,* and The Free Press of Glencoe, Inc.

JOHN CUMMING, M.D.
ELAINE CUMMING, PH.D.

Syracuse, N. Y.
June, 1962

Contents

PART II: THE STRUCTURE
OF THE MILIEU

PART III: EGO IN MILIEU

EGO & MILIEU

Introduction

THE BACKGROUND AND SCOPE OF THE BOOK

This book is both theoretical and practical. On the theoretical side, we attempt to synthesize some familiar psychological and sociological concepts into a new theory of how the ego functions—or fails to function—in its environment. Our theory concerns itself with ego growth and development insofar as it is necessary to the understanding of ego damage and ego restitution. On the practical side, we suggest how relatively unskilled people can be trained to create a therapeutic milieu for patients with serious illnesses: psychoses, senile confusion, brain damage, and severe neuroses. These practical skills, in turn, are embedded in and arise out of sociological theories of the environment.

In the past few years the term "milieu therapy" has become so popular that few hospitals will admit to *not* supplying a therapeutic milieu. Some hospitals, for example, record the treatment given to a psychotic patient who has received little more than three meals a day and a bed each night as milieu therapy. But what, in fact, is milieu therapy? And why has it become so popular to claim it?

Albert Deutsch [1] has described how beneficent environments for mentally ill patients have come and gone; whereas the use of the word "milieu" to mean a scientifically planned environment appears to have come into the literature during the

1

late thirties and early forties.* By 1953, David Rioch and
Alfred Stanton [3] had published a review article regarding the
promising new developments in milieu therapy. They started
with Harry Stack Sullivan's [4] classical observation that schizophrenics did not behave in a psychotic way when they were on
a ward staffed with sympathetic people. Sullivan's work appears
to have been the first serious attempt in the twentieth century
to investigate what Rioch and Stanton call "the nature of the
social matrix and its use in therapy."

It is instructive to observe the variety of programs which
are grouped together in this 1953 article; it gives substance to
a belief, widely held at the time, that "it doesn't much matter
what you do to mental hospital patients—they will improve as
long as you do *something*." We try in this book to provide a
coherent theoretical framework that will account for these past
successes, point to future inventions, and throw some new light
on ego function.

When we look at the early experiments in milieu therapy,
whether or not they were given that name, we notice a common
characteristic: almost all these experiments used psychological
or psychiatric theories, or parts of theories, of illness or dis-
ability and inferred from them what kinds of environments
would be most therapeutic. The most explicit example of this
phase is the Menningers' development of "prescribed" environments in which attitudes of staff and activities of the patient
were prescribed in terms of the individual patient's psychodynamic diagnosis.[5] In a sense, the Menningers were building
on Sullivan who, in his sensitivity to the schizophrenic process,
had worked out a way of selecting ward personnel with the
capacity to understand the patients' anxieties and to respect
their tangential communications. The Menningers, however,
made concrete and specific prescriptions for the environment.
Each patient was carefully diagnosed in terms of his psycho-

---

* See, for example, the work of Bettelheim and Sylvester.[2]

dynamic needs and a minutely detailed interpersonal environment was worked out for him. Furthermore, frequent evaluations of his progress were made and the environment was shifted as his needs shifted. Carrying out this plan required many staff members, and it rested upon two assumptions: that each patient could be treated separately in a private milieu tailored to his inner needs, and that any staff member could successfully assume the prescribed attitudes.*

At Chestnut Lodge, where Sullivan had worked, Frieda Fromm-Reichmann [7, 8] carried forward the therapeutic use of ward personnel. Others, following this tradition, developed a series of researches into the therapeutic power of the *total* environment, including the administrative structure.

This work at Chestnut Lodge culminated in the publication, in 1954, of *The Mental Hospital* by Alfred Stanton and Morris Schwartz.[9] These authors added a new ingredient to what was by then becoming a flood of reports of the good results from beneficent milieus. They discussed the milieu on equal terms with individual therapies and not simply as a complement to them. In other words, the environment can *itself* be the primary treatment as well as supporting or complementing other treatment. Although Stanton and Schwartz did not attach their work firmly to any theory of the social situation, their method of analyzing their data allows others to do so. Furthermore, they sometimes used failure of communication as an explanatory device, and in doing so eliminated alternative psychodynamic explanations. In a classical example, they pointed out that the patient, when he worries the staff for drinks of

---

* There is evidence in the work of Key [6] that the latter assumption was unwarranted. He says, "It appears from this finding that differences between activity therapist personalities are major determiners of patients' perceptions of activity therapists. Efforts on the part of activity therapists to adopt different roles with different patients are *apparently* ineffective and are overshadowed by the personality of the activity therapists." We shall, ourselves, offer a different hypothesis of why these staff members were unable to assume the appropriate attitudes.

water, may be just thirsty and not demanding attention. In short, they drew attention to the fact that the environment has properties that are irrelevant to psychodynamics but important to general welfare.

Since this pioneering study in social structure and patient care, William Caudill has contributed two analyses [10, 11] of the effect of culture, or organized values, norms, and customs, upon patient care. First, he delineated the culture of a small psychiatric hospital, emphasizing how different expectation and belief systems of patients and staff lead to therapeutic impasses. Next, he described how the total Japanese culture affects the care and treatment of the mentally ill in that country.

Thomas Freeman, John L. Cameron, and Andrew McGhie [12] have developed in detail the relationship between ego psychology and certain specific characteristics of the environment. They have shown how it is possible to trace the influence of certain episodes on the patient's mental state, and they have offered a theory of ego boundary maintenance to explain what they have seen. They have built an important new segment of theory, and we are in their debt.

Throughout this accumulated development of theory and practice there has been one notable lack. There has been a reluctance to consider the possibility that the milieu might itself bring about specific changes in the behavior of patients *and thus specific changes in their personalities.* Maxwell Jones, however, working in a somewhat specialized situation, has used the total interpersonal environment as his major therapeutic tool; but he is an exception.* Our failure to take sufficient account of the importance of the environment may, on the one

---

* Maxwell Jones [13] developed his theory of the therapeutic community while working with patients diagnosed as having sociopathic disorders. These are people who have difficulty understanding the effect of their actions on others. Our theory is complementary to Jones' as it was developed mainly in work with schizophrenics, and these are patients who have difficulty acting at all.

hand, have its roots in our long tradition of focusing on the biological unit, the individual. On the other hand, it may be because we do not have a viable theory of how the milieu achieves its therapeutic ends.

We shall attempt to tie together these themes and concepts and develop a theory that will enable us to practice a milieu therapy which is *a scientific manipulation of the environment aimed at producing changes in the personality of the patient.* This theory will have to be general enough to include social structure, culture, and personality, all in the same terms. To do this we must be able to move from discussions of the environment to discussions of personality through an articulating set of concepts expressed in terms common to the whole theoretical formulation. No one seems to have put forward a general theory, except for Talcott Parsons,[14] whose general theory of action, although very suggestive and helpful, does not lend itself very easily to operations. We shall, however, draw upon the theories of a number of social scientists and psychiatrists in our own attempt to develop a general formulation.

In Part I of this book we shall set forth a theory of ego function. In Part II we shall discuss illustrations of the use of the theory in the treatment of the mentally ill. In Part III we shall try to give an idea of the dynamics of the interaction of ego and milieu and discuss the future applications of the theory, especially in community-based programs. We shall conclude with some theoretical, ethical, and pragmatic problems that are raised by the theory and that need solution. Parts II and III of this book are related to Part I conceptually, but the reader whose interest lies primarily in the applications of the theory can read Parts II and III independently. Some may wish to read them first and then return to the theory.

References

[1] ALBERT DEUTSCH, *The Mentally Ill in America* (New York: Columbia University Press, 1937).

[2] BRUNO BETTELHEIM and EMMY SYLVESTER, "A Therapeutic Milieu," *American Journal of Orthopsychiatry*, 18 (1948), 191.

[3] DAVID McK. RIOCH and ALFRED H. STANTON, "Milieu Therapy," *Psychiatric Treatment*, Vol. XXI—proceedings of the Association for Research in Nervous and Mental Disease (Baltimore: Williams and Wilkins, 1953).

[4] HARRY STACK SULLIVAN, "Socio-psychiatric Research: Its Implications for the Schizophrenia Problem and for Mental Hygiene," *American Journal of Psychiatry*, 10 (1931), 977.

[5] W. C. MENNINGER, "Psychoanalytic Principles in Psychiatric Hospital Therapy," *Southern Medical Journal*, 32 (1939), 348.

[6] WILLIAM H. KEY, "Coordination of the Ancillary Therapies," in M. Greenblatt and B. Simon (eds.), *Rehabilitation of the Mentally Ill* (Washington, D.C.: American Association for the Advancement of Science, 1959).

[7] FRIEDA FROMM-REICHMANN, "Remarks on the Philosophy of Mental Disorder," *Psychiatry*, 9 (1946), 293.

[8] ———, *Principles of Intensive Psychotherapy* (Chicago: University of Chicago Press, 1950).

6

[9] ALFRED STANTON and MORRIS SCHWARTZ, *The Mental Hospital* (New York: Basic Books, 1954).

[10] WILLIAM CAUDILL, *The Psychiatric Hospital as a Small Society* (Cambridge, Mass.: Harvard University Press, 1958).

[11] ———, "Around the Clock Patient Care in Japanese Psychiatric Hospitals: The Role of the Tsukisoi," *American Sociological Review,* 26 (April 1961), 204.

[12] THOMAS FREEMAN, JOHN L. CAMERON, and ANDREW McGHIE, *Chronic Schizophrenia* (New York: International Universities Press, 1958).

[13] MAXWELL JONES, *The Therapeutic Community* (New York: Basic Books, 1953).

[14] TALCOTT PARSONS, *The Social System* (Glencoe, Ill.: Free Press, 1951).

PART I

THE EGO

CHAPTER 1

Some Usable Concepts
of Ego in the Milieu

In this chapter we shall draw together a number of ideas available to us through the work of others and reformulate them in a way that will allow us to discuss the person in the situation * in practical terms.

For these purposes, it is important to have a set of concepts that embrace both personality and situation. For example, the Oedipus complex, a totally *interior* notion, is of little help in discussing the milieu in which a man suffering from this affliction can best be treated. Psychoanalytic concepts are directed toward telling us *how* the individual perceives life, and the general *tone* of his behavior, but these concepts have little strength in predicting specifically what he will *do*. Thus, a man who suffers from castration fear may see all men in authority as punitive and threatening, and the general feeling and attitude he will have toward these men will be predictable; but whether or not he will be able, in spite of this, to maintain

---

* The word "situation" will be used interchangeably with the words "environment" and "milieu" throughout.

a stable job performance is a different question, one whose answer requires additional concepts with other frames of reference for its formulation.

Although traditional psychoanalytic concepts can inform us about tendencies toward action, they tell us little about how an act will be performed or even if it will be performed at all. It is with the latter that we are concerned. However, a number of concepts that have grown out of traditional psychoanalysis—often grouped together as "ego psychology"—are useful in thinking of the sick person in his milieu. Because these concepts conceive the ego as the point at which the person meets the situation, they can help us to answer the question of whether or not he will be able to act, and, if he can, whether or not his acts will be appropriate. We shall assume throughout that patients who are restored to interpersonal and occupational competence are no longer ill; but we explicitly exclude the assumption that personality can be conceived as pathological while behavior persists as normal.

In this book, we shall primarily be interested in linking the concept of the ego to theories of the milieu; therefore, we shall deal less with the *ontogeny* of the ego than with its *properties*.* We shall first discuss the ego in a quasi-historical manner, using only certain contributions from a variety of theorists. We do not attempt a systematic comparison of ego psychologies, nor a survey of them, but rather a synthesis of certain aspects of various theories into a utilitarian whole. Furthermore, it is possible that we have totally neglected certain theories that converge with those we have used, and we have certainly not attempted to do justice to the whole work of any of the writers whose concepts we have used. We have selected from each source certain ideas which, when put together and elaborated, provide a core of theory from which we can deduce

---

* A lucid summary of the psychoanalytic theory of the development of the ego has been given by Freeman, Cameron, and McGhie.[1]

useful corollaries. The following discussion will try to pull together the main features of the ideas of the structure and function of the ego as they have been developed by several authors. We shall present these concepts in such a way as to emphasize an idea latent in some theories, explicit in others: the ego grows through a series of successfully resolved crises each of which disturbs a temporary equilibrium but leads to reorganization at a higher level. The ego may thus be thought of as in a moving, steady state.

HARTMANN'S CONCEPT OF A CONFLICT-FREE PORTION OF THE EGO

Traditionally, the ego was considered, as Freud [2] postulated, to compromise between conflicting impulses and demands. It was conceived as uniting in some kind of workable harmony the imperious demands of the id and the equally imperious strictures of both the superego and the environment. The ego in this view is an arbitrator, a transmuter, and a synthesizer establishing priorities and changing undesirable impulses into acceptable ones.

Heinz Hartmann [3] enlarged Freud's original concept of the ego. He did not believe that it arose, as Freud conceived it, in conflict between the id, superego, and reality, with only the function of synthesizer. Hartmann recognized a "conflict-free portion"—that is, a part which developed from the natural endowment of the individual and which was not dependent on the classical Freudian joust for its existence. This portion he conceived as being the individual's native competences—his ability to walk and to speak, as well as the inborn talents that he brings to bear on problems needing solution. He believed that instrumental tasks were performed under the direction of this conflict-free portion of the ego. His reasoning was based partly upon the observation that children develop the skills of speech and thought and locomotion under widely differing environmental circumstances and, therefore, that a "built-in" plan rather than psychic conflict seemed to be operating to produce them. The plan is conceived as built-in in the sense of a certain potential being present which requires certain environmental minima in order to emerge. The environment, therefore, governs the details of the emergent qualities but not the ground-plan. This is the concept often referred to as an "epigenetic plan" of development.

When all of the emergent capacities—thought, perception, intention, comprehension of objects, motor development, and so on—are taken together, they form the conflict-free structure of the ego whose function we know as "executive." * It follows that individuals must vary according to their native endowment and that biological energy itself is a determinant of personality since it affects the executive function.

Innate skills will usually lie latent until propitious circumstances † present themselves, but the manner and degree of their development are sensitive to the social environment. Furthermore, there is reason to suspect from animal studies that certain skills may sometimes be lost if they are not developed at the propitious time.‡

On the whole, the uniformity with which skills such as walking and speech develop speaks for an epigenetic origin. They might be expected to be much more variable in their development if they were conflict-born, and a much more obvious gradation of competence in such things as walking and talking should match gradations in the effectiveness of the resolution of the conflict.

Hartmann and others, then, conceived the ego as partly

---

* Freud recognized the executive function of the ego, but he did not work out its origins in detail.

† Davis [4] reports a child brought up in extreme isolation who lacked both speech and locomotion at the age of eight and yet caught up with her age mates when given special training.

‡ See, for example, the work of Scott.[5]

formed by important talents emerging from biological sources and nourished by biological energy. When these talents are exercised in appropriate socio-cultural situations, they grow to their maximum potential. Thus, psychologists have characterized the ego as being partly conflict-born and synthetic in function and partly conflict-free and executive in function, with the whole structure sensitive to the environment for maximum development.

An important question about the nature of the ego persists. Why does it function at all? Why do people do difficult things for little reward? Why does a child, once having learned to walk, continue to walk? Freud believed, and some modern theorists such as Gardner Murphy [6] and the various learning theorists * agree, that the drive to reduce tension pushes a child along. The latter group differs from Freud and his followers only in its concept of the origin of tension. Freud sees this tension arising in the two great drives, Eros and Thanatos, whereas the others postulate thousands of specific "tissue tensions." In this view, behavior is caused by the anticipation of the pleasure accompanying the lowering of that tension. This explanation has never been acceptable to a still different group of theorists that includes Gordon Allport [8] and H. A. Murray,[9] who argue that it does not account for any of the outgoing, reaching, initiating, or "proacting" behaviors that are so essentially human, even if it is agreed that the organism might deliberately raise tension in order to lower it. No one of the drive theories seems totally satisfactory for the understanding of human behavior. Nevertheless, abandoning them usually leads to concepts that are indistinguishable from them except in name. We do not reject the idea of drive in this theory, but it will not be prominent. It can be assumed that some theory of drive is necessary to account for ego energy and motivation

---

* See, for example, the work of Hilgard and Marquis.[7]

Freudian theory itself gives us many examples of primary drives supplying energy for purposes far different from the original objects. Our theory is concerned less with drives than with the apparatus through which these drives are directed into action. We are interested in the influence that social factors have on the expression of impulse, and in how social influences are used in the attainment of drive satisfaction. Our own theory and drive theory are not incompatible, and if it appears useful to do so, it will be possible to articulate them.

Because of our focus on action, we have found Robert White's recent modification of drive theory to be useful.[10] He has proposed an innate impulse toward competence, which he terms "effectance motivation." He sees this as acting independently of the libidinous drives, as in instrumental activity, or in double harness with them, as when the individual takes pride in the flair and style with which he satisfies his instinctual drives.

This idea of White's has familiar overtones. George Homans,[11] paraphrasing Elton Mayo, who in turn is "making Aristotle's point," says: ". . . there is a tendency for any group of men to complicate the conditions of their life, [and] to make the conditions more interesting. . . . any circumstances interfering with the complication [are] felt emotionally as frustration." Despite its antiquity, David Rapaport * argues—albeit tortuously—that the evidence upon which White rests his competence drive can be explained more parsimoniously by the Freudian primary drives. On the whole, we think that the class of outreaching actions White seeks to explain is so important that the idea of a special drive is heuristic, inasmuch as it draws attention to these outreaching actions as primary, rather than derived, human attributes.

Another group of theorists has emphasized the importance

---

* In a discussion of White's [10] work.

for motivation of the culture, especially the value system. Authors such as Karen Horney,[12] Clara Thompson,[13] and Erich Fromm [14] have focused on the interpersonal and cultural impact of the others in the situation. Harry Stack Sullivan [15] made an early and systematic attempt to build a theory that would account for schizophrenia, which he conceived as an interpersonal failure.

No one of these authors, however, has dealt in a systematic way with the effects of the environment upon the developing ego. But Hartmann realized that the two "portions" of the ego—the conflict-born and the conflict-free—were mutually interdependent; and, because of this interdependence, he perceived the importance of the environment in the development of the ego. Thus, if the synthetic function of the ego is not developing well and thus the id impulses are not under good control, the executive function has difficulty emerging. It is a truism that if a child has developed an inappropriately punitive superego, he may not be able to learn so well or so much as he would be able to if he did not have this source of guilt and anxiety, and, as a result, he will not fully realize his complement of inherent skills. In this way, a hampered or weak synthetic function results in an improperly developed executive function, and thus the integrity of the ego must be viewed holistically.

What has *not* been so clearly recognized in the past is that the well-being of the ego is also affected in a reverse way. If a child has learned a wide variety of such skills as reading, manipulating objects, writing, running, and doing arithmetic, he has an armamentarium of practical, problem-solving skills that will strengthen his executive function and will thus provide him with a variety of possible solutions to the conflicts with which the synthetic function must deal.* Furthermore, a child will

---

* This, of course, implies a correlation between ego strength and education—a testable implication.

have a wider perspective on problems and will be aware of
more ways in which they can be approached. An intellectually
competent child is therefore likely to find acceptable outlets
for his impulses, because, when accrued skills result in a
stronger executive function, the conflict-born portion of the
ego will be subjected to less stress. This does not imply that
intellectual development as such has ego-strengthening properties but rather that intellectual development leads to com-
petency which in turn fortifies ego structure.

The ego can be looked upon as a unitary structure functioning not only to placate imperious biological drives and
inescapable social demands but also to invent patterns of intrinsically rewarding action.

The way the person comes to perform appropriately in a
wide variety of situations is usually known as "adjustment" or
"adaptation." * This adaptation not only symbolizes continuity
because it is the act of accepting the situation created by past
generations of men, but it also contributes to the situation and
thus changes the environment, if only imperceptibly. In this
sense, adaptation is a two-way process in which the individual
reorganizes himself to accommodate to the milieu and at the
same time influences that milieu. In this formulation, Hartmann converges upon two other important schools of thinking:
the interpersonal school of Sullivan, and the existentialist
school with its emphasis upon the effect of the individual's
choice upon the environment.[16] The holistic ego thus finds, in
adaptation, creative outlets that in turn are reflected in the
face of the general culture.

ERIKSON'S CONCEPT OF EGO IDENTITY

Erik Erikson,[17] writing two decades later than Hartmann,
recognized the importance to the individual of variations in

---

* For some time "adjustment" has been a "bad" word and "adaptation" a "good" word, but we use them interchangeably.

the situation and, therefore, addressed himself to the problem of the ego developing in a society. He concluded that the development of "ego identity"—an essential ingredient of the intact and healthy ego—requires a "successful alignment" of basic drives, individual endowments, and the situation—that is, of the impulse life, the synthetic *and* executive portions of the ego, *and* the opportunities in the situation. He was, then, the first to give equivalent value to the environment. He believed that only harmony among all four elements would allow the individual to maintain a sense of continuity, both of himself and of the situation. When he achieves this harmony, the person has ". . . the accrued confidence that [his] ability to maintain inner sameness and continuity . . . is matched by the sameness and continuity of [his] meaning for others." A child who learns to know and master himself and the world has a sense of himself as one who is capable of handling a predictable environment.

Like Hartmann, Erikson believes that there is some epigenesis in the development of the ego—much of it is "built-in" and needs only the proper circumstances in which to emerge to full potentiality. But he adds his own concept of identifiable crisis points in development. A child, in his view, increases both his skills and his drives as he matures, but, at the same time, society makes culturally determined demands of him and signifies culturally approved opportunities for action. For example, at a certain point in his life, a child must go to school, and there he may further increase his mastery of the environment. Such changes may coincide with more fundamental epigenetic phases of development, and these inner and outer changes together will require major reorientations on the part of the child, both to himself and to the world around him. These needs for reorientation are essentially problems to be solved. If he solves each problem adequately as he meets it, a child will be better able to solve the next—in short, his ego will be stronger and more capable of further problem solution.

If the child fails to resolve one crisis, his ego remains weak and less able to resolve the next one. Thus, Erikson gives us the idea of growth through crisis resolution.

Erikson added to the idea of ego adaptation a further idea of ego feeling. This concept was developed earlier by Paul Federn.[18] It is a sufficiently important concept to warrant separate treatment, and we shall return to it again; but, in the meantime, we note that when Erikson speaks of a "sense" which is a pervasive, affective tone accompanying the state of ego identity—or its opposite, ego diffusion—he approximates Federn very closely. He contributes, however, the specific idea of ego identity producing a feeling of appropriateness and satisfaction or even euphoria, whereas ego diffusion is experienced unpleasantly as a disjunction between self and society.

We can, as we accumulate these ideas, conceive of the ego as a product of both biological characteristics and the encounter with emergent problems. As the person adapts to the environment, he modifies it at the same time, partly through spontaneous creative acts. In doing so he achieves a certain harmony with the interpersonal and cultural situation.

MEAD'S CONCEPT OF THE GENERALIZED OTHER

We turn now to those theories of personality that are concerned with how a child learns to act in roles. George Herbert Mead [19] was impressed with the apparent ease with which children take part in complex systems of interaction. In trying to understand this ability, he proposed that role learning must be a double process in which both members of an interacting pair learn both roles. When a boy and his father are together, the father is constantly revealing through various cues the kinds of behavior he thinks appropriate for a son. The son, in order to be able to respond appropriately to his father, must learn a good deal about his father's motives and feelings. His ability to perceive what his father expects of him in any situation means that he has also learned something of the father role. By the same token, the father relives his earlier role of son to his own father in the course of interacting with his child. In this way, the two come to understand each other and to act firmly in their own roles while "taking the role of the other" in order to understand the interaction.

Mead observed that the same principle of learning extended beyond the two-person relationship and eventually included the "generalized other." If, for example, a baseball player cannot predict what all eight of his fellow players are likely to do, he cannot play. Although he acts as an individual, his action must be such that it is appropriate to the concerted action of nine persons. When a boy finally enters his first job, his success will depend in part upon his ability to muster the appropriate elements of an intricate organization of past role experiences centered upon task performance. His abilities as a baseball player may in the end be the most important antecedent to his first job.

PARSONS' CONCEPT OF SOCIALIZATION

Talcott Parsons [20] talks of growth and development in terms similar to Mead's, but like Hartmann and Erikson, he assumes emergent, biologically given capacities and periodic interruptions of stable equilibriums by these capacities. Parsons' description of ego development departs from the others in postulating the need for a certain essential minimum of differentiation in the environment in order for a child's emerging abilities to develop and function adequately in his society. His theory postulates the development of a child's personality through development of a role repertoire by "internalization" of the adults in the environment. Through a process of assigning familiar objects into finer and finer categories, a child learns to discriminate the appropriate relationships first between himself and his mother, later between the sexes, between adults and

children, between his family and those outside of it, and, finally, between people to whom he relates in terms of their performance in their roles and those to whom he relates in terms of their intrinsic qualities.* Equally important, he learns the *relationships* among all these roles, so that he incorporates them as his personality or ego organization and so is able to interact meaningfully with others, even when he is in a group who are interacting among themselves as well as with him. As he learns all these distinctions, a child "internalizes" them in an orderly way. Parsons has thus taken Mead's idea of "learning the role of the generalized other" and has refined its inner structure. †
By doing so, he is able to specify the dimensions of the adult personality in the same terms as adult social roles. Furthermore, the organization of personality in this view reflects the organization of society, because both are built up of the relationships between people acting in roles, first, in the nuclear family and, later, in the greater society. The ego is so organized that the individual, with comparative ease, can assume all the major roles in society: spouse, parent, worker, friend, and so on. This concept also adds content to Erikson's idea of ego identity, and it can be used to specify areas of failure in identity —that is, diffusion. Thus, in Parsons' view, a child, learning both his own and the other person's part in any set of interactions, is supplied with an ego structure sufficiently complex and flexible to enable him to solve the problems of living in society. Parsons' formulation implies that only through this process of learning the full complement of social roles will the child achieve a firm identity. Failure of role learning at any

---

* At the same time, a child is developing an image of himself in different roles, as he sees it reflected in his interactions with others.

† Only part of Parsons' theory of socialization is used here, and therefore it appears to be oversimplified. For example, we do not refer to the phase in which the child has a dyadic relationship with the mother, and we do not introduce the idea of the child being an object to himself. It should be assumed throughout that the self is always an object to the ego.

point will leave him unable to organize the various "internalized others" in a way that will allow him to act in the roles prescribed for adults. The refinements of perception and inner organization and the enhancements of ability to take roles are both conceived as occurring at an ontogenetic crisis similar to those recognized by Freud, as well as by Hartmann, Erikson, and other ego psychologists. Parsons, again using Mead's basic concept, contributes textural richness to the scheme by suggesting how the actual structure of society becomes meaningful to a child, and hence manageable. Furthermore, Parsons' theory suggests why, for adequate socialization, it is so necessary for the parents to have full membership in their own society: only if they do can the child learn a variety of role relationships.

LEWIN'S CONCEPT OF GROWTH

As early as 1941, Kurt Lewin [21] was developing an idea of growth as a two-phase process. In his theory, the individual was conceived as a point in a field of forces, and this field was called "lifespace"—a concept with points of similarity to our idea of ego. Lewin conceived of the lifespace as containing differentiated areas which became more numerous as a child grew older. As areas are added to the lifespace, integration among them is taking place; the lifespace, thus, has an interdependence of its parts or, as Lewin called it, unity. Growth, to Lewin, implied both differentiation and integration.

This is an important concept for us. It suggests, for example, that the complex of learned role interrelationships that Parsons describes does not automatically organize itself but requires an active process of simultaneously internalizing new role relationships and integrating them with those already internalized. Furthermore, it raises a question about the nature of this integration. If a person learns some role relationships in considerable detail and neglects others, can the over-all integration of these ego elements somehow compensate for this

uneven complexity and strength? Such a compensating integration might be analogous to the way in which the complex
chemical organization of the body can compensate for low
levels of certain vital chemicals by using higher levels of related
ones. In other words, can integration compensate for uneven
differentiation? We shall return to this point in the following
chapter.

Lewin's formulation also suggests that there must be a
certain degree of dedifferentiation of existing attitudes, knowledge, and affects before new knowledge, attitudes, and affects
can become functioning parts of the ego. This idea implies that
at the time of epigenetic crisis there may be a partial dissolution
of what has been learned, with a subsequent reorganization to
include the new elements. Such a dissolution assumes an
openness that results from new learning and, at the same time,
makes it possible for the developing child to incorporate it.
This concept of temporary disintegration adumbrates Erikson's
concept of epigenetic crisis with its vulnerability to failure—
particularly ego diffusion.

Thus far we have not discussed the affective or sensory
qualities of the ego in a direct way. We shall, therefore, attempt
to relate Federn's concept of "ego feeling" to the concepts of
the structure and function of the ego discussed above.

FEDERN'S CONCEPT OF EGO FEELING

Ego structure and ego strength are constructs inferred from
behavior. In contrast, ego feeling is primarily a subjective, experienced state which appears to mediate between the self,
perceived as self, and the environment.* Ego feeling is curiously
difficult to talk about—we do not seem to have the language.
Federn calls it ". . . self-experience . . . which is not an

---

* Ego feeling can, of course, be inferred by observers. It is experienced by people and, possibly, sympathetically induced in others, but it
is also subject to inference.

abstraction but a reality. It is an entity which stands in relation to the continuity of the person in respect to time, space, and causality. It can be recognized objectively and is constantly felt and perceived subjectively." We possess, in other words, an enduring feeling and knowledge that our ego is continuous and persistent, despite interruptions by sleep, forgetting, or un-consciousness, because we feel that processes within us have a persistent origin. Federn, thus, includes in ego feeling both mentation, or consciousness, and feeling. He says explicitly that ". . . the ego's experience of itself does not consist simply in the knowledge and consciousness of the qualities of the ego . . . the experience also includes a sensory element for which the words 'feeling' or 'sensation' are appropriate." Ego feeling, then, is permanently colored with affect and is more than just self-consciousness.*

Federn believes that an important inherent quality of ego feeling is its persistence through time; after an interruption, normal people recognize ego feeling as the same feeling that they had been experiencing before.

A final important property of ego feeling is that it is bounded. Federn says, "Whenever there is a change in ego feeling cathexis, we sense the 'boundaries' of our ego." (*Ego Psychology and the Psychoses,* p. 64.) Any stimulus that impinges upon the person arouses ego feeling or a sense of self. Federn uses the term "cathexis" to describe the flow of ego feeling or energy which greets a stimulus and determines its relation to the self and, hence, in turn, modifies ego feeling. The ego

---

* Federn thinks of ego feeling as a concrete reality that can be both recognized objectively and perceived subjectively. It also validates the existence of the ego. (" . . . the familiar phenomenon of the ego feeling . . . proves the existence of the ego." *Ego Psychology and the Psychoses,* p. 212.) Although it seems to us that ego feeling as Federn describes it cannot validate an ego any more than it can validate the presence of a soul or a homunculus as the organizing principle of human behavior, his ideas in general have great heuristic value.

boundary may thus be thought of as a surface which is characteristically in touch with a wide range of stimuli. The ego boundary must be thought of as unequally involved over its area, inasmuch as there may be more ego energy in some parts of it than others. For example, a person sitting and talking with a friend may be conscious of a number of other stimuli—the wind in the trees, the fire dying down, the sound of children talking in another part of the house. These other stimuli are unambiguous, and he has sufficient ego involvement with them to retain a clear feeling of himself as separate from but related meaningfully to them, but his strongest ego involvement or cathexis, or attention, is with the friend with whom he is engaged in conversation.

This conception of the ego boundary as a superordinate sense organ—the place where stimuli are received, interpreted in the light of previous ego content, and internalized and reorganized as part of the ego—suggests an ego mechanism consonant with Lewin's idea of dedifferentiation and growth.

To recapitulate: ego feeling is related conceptually to ego identity; it is a consistent, conscious, affective awareness of self, both as a psychic and as a physical entity, persistent over time, and recognizably reconstituted after an interruption. The boundaries of ego feeling are receptive to stimuli and are fluid in the sense of being unevenly invested throughout with energy or attention. The ego boundary appears to supply a coherent, stable feeling of selfness and sameness and may be the affective "organ" of ego identity.

Any object, concept, norm, or event repeatedly experienced at the ego boundary seems eventually, to use Federn's term, to be "egotized." That is, the interpretation of the object, concept, norm, or event becomes part of the person experiencing it—a differentiated part of his ego. In this sense a loss from the usual, expected external environment is always a loss of part of the self.

Federn has talked about ego feeling among normal people only in terms of its rather dramatic appearances and disappearances during sleeping, dreaming, and waking. It is likely, however, that it varies considerably in the ordinary course of events and that it may even suffer periodic disruptions that are "phenocopies" of the major disruptions which characterize the psychoses.

There is evidence from the many studies of sensory deprivation [22] that a certain level of stimulation must be maintained in order for identity feeling to remain intact. It appears that the figure must have a ground, that existence must always be reinforced, and, perhaps, that we can know the world only through change. These speculations, however, take us into the area of neurological correlates of experience, and we are not qualified to proceed; nor, for the pragmatic purposes of this book, is it necessary that we do.

Freeman, Cameron, and McGhie [1] have discussed, in *Chronic Schizophrenia*, some of the problems of managing schizophrenia in terms of ego boundary, and they have shown interesting evidence of the difficulty that schizophrenics experience, under conditions of ambiguity, in distinguishing between themselves and others.* Edward Bibring [23] has described the "emptying" of the ego in depression and the sensation of the "draining" of self-esteem which is experienced. All these evidences of disruption of ego feeling and ego boundaries in the acute illnesses fail to account for variations in normal ego feeling.

Some people seem to be more acutely aware than others are, of ego boundaries, and some are more prone toward feelings of dispersion or diffusion. There is preliminary intuitive evidence

---

* Although these authors have a psychodynamic explanation for this failure, it seems to us to be more usefully thought of in terms of failure to make the first distinction in Parsons' scheme—that is, to distinguish between oneself and others.

that some people when in crisis suffer from feelings of alienation, depersonalization, or loss of boundary, whereas others
suffer from feelings of deflation, emptiness, and collapse. There
may eventually be a systematic language for discussing these
feelings; in the meantime, it is worth noting that there do
seem to be differences that probably have analogues in the
subjective experiences of people with different kinds of psychoses.

RECAPITULATION OF SELECTED CONCEPTS

The concept of ego is formulated differently by the various
authors from whom we have borrowed, but there are cores of
common meaning in each of them. First, ego is conceived as an
interdependent combination of emergent abilities and conflict-
born elements. Second, the development of the ego is commonly regarded as occurring through a series of crises. These
crises appear to occur whenever the emergent skills and developing powers of a child need to be controlled, elaborated, or
enhanced, in order for him to be considered a normal member
of the culture. When these crises occur, the equilibrium of a
child's personality and of the system around him is partly upset.
A child's developing ego may be temporarily less differentiated
and less well organized, and his relationship to his environment
less concordant, until the crisis is resolved. This resolution
leaves the ego enhanced; growth has occurred. At the same time,
a child gets increasingly diverse types of roles. Each time he
successfully resolves a crisis or learns to assume a new role,
his ego is strengthened because he has internalized a new set
of interrelationships, increased his power of discrimination and,
perhaps, of hierarchizing, and has added to his knowledge of
the world and of himself.

The mechanism through which the world becomes affectively comprehensible—and, hence, through which learning is

possible—may be ego feeling at the boundary. This feeling, or cathexis, seems to act at the boundary between the individual and the environment as the organ through which the affective aspects of the world are sensed, sorted, classified, and ultimately known. Ego boundary and ego feeling may also provide the sharp and immediate sense of self as separate from the world, without which action cannot proceed effectively.

References

[1] THOMAS FREEMAN, JOHN L. CAMERON, and ANDREW McGHIE, *Chronic Schizophrenia* (New York: International Universities Press, 1958).

[2] SIGMUND FREUD, *The Ego and the Id* (London: Hogarth Press, 1946).

[3] HEINZ HARTMANN, *Ego Psychology and the Problem of Adaptation* (New York: International Universities Press, 1958).

[4] KINGSLEY DAVIS, "Final Note on a Case of Extreme Isolation," *American Journal of Sociology,* 52 (1947), 432.

[5] JOHN PAUL SCOTT, *Animal Behavior* (Chicago: University of Chicago Press, 1958).

[6] GARDNER MURPHY, *Personality, a Biosocial Approach* (New York: Harper, 1947).

[7] ERNEST R. HILGARD and DONALD G. MARQUIS, *Conditioning and Learning* (New York: Appleton-Century, 1940).

[8] GORDON ALLPORT, *Personality and Social Encounter* (Boston: Beacon Press, 1960).

[9] H. A. MURRAY, and others, *Explorations in Personality* (New York: Oxford University Press, 1938).

[10] ROBERT W. WHITE, "Competence and the Psychosexual

Stages of Development," *The Nebraska Symposium on Motivation* (Lincoln: University of Nebraska Press, 1960).

[11] GEORGE HOMANS, *The Human Group* (New York: Harcourt, Brace, 1950), p. 108.

[12] KAREN HORNEY, *New Ways in Psychoanalysis* (New York: W. W. Norton, 1939).

[13] CLARA THOMPSON, *Psychoanalysis: Evolution and Development* (New York: Hermitage House, 1950).

[14] ERICH FROMM, "Individual and Social Origins of Neurosis," *American Sociological Review*, 9 (1944), 380.

[15] HARRY STACK SULLIVAN, *The Interpersonal Theory of Psychiatry* (New York: W. W. Norton, 1953).

[16] ROLLO MAY, and others, *Existence* (New York: Basic Books, 1958).

[17] ERIK ERIKSON, *Childhood and Society* (New York: W. W. Norton, 1950).

[18] PAUL FEDERN, *Ego Psychology and the Psychoses* (New York: Basic Books, 1952).

[19] GEORGE HERBERT MEAD, *Mind, Self, and Society* (Chicago: University of Chicago Press, 1934).

[20] TALCOTT PARSONS and ROBERT F. BALES, *Family, Socialization and Interaction Process* (Glencoe, Ill.: Free Press, 1955).

[21] KURT LEWIN, *Field Theory in Social Sciences* (New York: Harper, 1951).

[22] PHILIP SOLOMON, and others, *Sensory Deprivation* (Cambridge, Mass.: Harvard University Press, 1961).

[23] EDWARD BIBRING, "The Mechanism of Depression," in Phyllis Greenacre (ed.), *Affective Disorders* (New York: International Universities Press, 1953).

CHAPTER 2

Ego Organization

We shall now attempt to regroup some of the ideas discussed in the previous chapter into one general concept of the relationship of the ego, viewed as a whole, to the milieu. Central to this conception will be the idea of *ego organization*. We shall introduce the term *ego set* to denote an element of ego organization, and we shall suggest ways in which the major outlines of ego organization may be laid down during socialization. We shall then consider the process of adaptation to the environment and advance the hypothesis that this involves changes in ego organization and accompanying changes in feeling tone. Later, in Chapter 4, we shall suggest ways in which the ego, as we conceive it, solves ordinary problems and some of the ways in which it may fail during pathological states.

EGO SETS

In our view, the unit of the ego is an *internal representation of a constellation or sequence of events experienced as part of an environment with a specific affective tone*. This representation, which is conceived as having a corresponding underlying pattern of neurological activation, we shall call an *ego set*. It is important that this unit is not a small structural building block but, rather, an organization through short periods of time of experiential elements. It is equally important that it is simple, and not a massively complex unit such as "the internalized role model."

Ego sets are assumed to be general in function since they can be used in a variety of specific situations and in combination with other sets. Thus, the organization of countless fragments of interaction, role playing, ideas, and sensations might result in a group of sets that, taken together, correspond to "my relationship with my aunt." This group of sets might then be generalized to "a relationship with an older female who belongs to my intimate circle," or it might be used in combination with other sets to produce "my kindred on my mother's side." These ego sets—like Lewin's lifespace areas—are assumed to be strengthened and differentiated in interaction. At the same time, they become more numerous and their organization, or integration, becomes more complex. Furthermore, if White is correct in positing a motivation toward competence, there should be a general human tendency to use new sets in old situations—rather than always to cling to those that have been successful in the past and, as a result, to develop even more complex organizations.

Role learning, in this view, is general rather than specific, and this implies that the ego is able to apportion ego sets into complex organizations and thus is able to meet new role demands. These organizations are built from elements learned in interaction with numerous role models. At the same time, organized patterns of these sets of internalized role elements are constantly used in dealing with the milieu.

ORGANIZATION OF SETS

We shall now return to an idea, common to the work of Mead, Lewin, and Parsons, that some form of inner organization is essential for social action. Mead, it will be recalled, postulated that a child, in order to act in his own role, must learn to take the roles of those with whom he interacts. In the same vein, Parsons argues that a developing child learns both sides of all the relationships in the nuclear family in an orderly sequence. He therefore becomes able to interact effectively with all the members either singly or together. Later he learns to relate directly to his peers and, later still, to the world of work and contract. He has, of course, experienced adumbrations of these interactions. For example, if he has ever visited his father at his place of business, a child has begun to learn the task-oriented part of the father's set of roles.*

A child must finally achieve an inner organization of the relationships among the roles of others in order to behave appropriately in any social context, and *in a general way, he must organize all manner of objects, ideas, events, and values into a coherent system.*† We have discussed in some detail in Chapter 1 how the elements of roles may be internalized. It seems probable, as Parsons has said (in *The Social System,* p. 210), that a process of discrimination allows a child to select certain aspects of an object as the special target of this involvement and then, by a process of generalization, to become attached to that aspect of other people and, finally, to the idea of the aspect. For example, he may come to believe that "warmth" is an important human quality and to have an emotional investment in this belief.

Furthermore, as Anthony Wallace [2] has suggested, habitual ways of doing things become egotized in the same way that

---

* For the idea of "role sets" see the work of Merton.[1]

† This terminology has problems. A set is the simplest unit of the ego in this formulation, but the set itself is an organization of elements. Furthermore, an ego organization is an organization of sets and can be thought of as a master set. We shall attempt to use the words "set" and "ego set" to mean relatively small organized units, and "organization" to mean systems of more than one set. All the terms are, in the end, arbitrary.

relationships and objects do. He suggests that this is how cultural patterns come to be held so dear. Such organizations seem to be fundamental to the efficient handling of the environment. In fact, no matter what mechanism is used for learning them, such organizations seem to be essentially human in character.

Ego organization, then, must articulate ideas, objects, and potential action—or, rather, their representations—into a coherent whole. To look at role learning in these terms would lead us to suppose, for example, that a child who has never interacted with adults having work roles will be handicapped in discriminating between the behaviors appropriate for interacting with people who share such general and acquired criteria as "one of the class of people who lay bricks" and those behaviors appropriate for interacting with people who share the particular and inborn criterion of "belonging to our family." Such a child will find that none of the sets acquired in familial role relationships will be entirely appropriate in a work situation; he may then become the victim of the kind of conflict over authority that comes from relationships in which the boss is mistaken for the father. By the same token, a child who does not well distinguish the culturally assigned roles of men and women will be confused about sex-role behavior. In both cases, imperfect socialization can be thought of as leading to an inadequate variety of sets or poorly differentiated sets, and hence to less general ego organizations.*

RESPONSE TO CHANGE AND ADAPTATION

Flux and change is the normal state of human beings. The continual, smooth rapprochement between the individual and

---

* We make the assumption that poorly differentiated sets cannot be too well organized because of the process by which they become differentiated in the first place. In other words unless they are differentiated, there is no basis for articulating them.

his environment is adaptation. It is only when changes are of an unusual order that adaptation becomes a conscious process. An early formulation of W. I. Thomas says that ". . . when influences appear to disrupt habits, when new stimuli demand action, when the habitual situation is altered, or when the individual or group is unprepared for an experience, then the phenomenon assumes the aspect of a crisis." [3] In our terms, it seems probable that the ego must have a certain minimum variety of elements and a certain minimum generality of organization in order not to experience change as a crisis. Furthermore, the environment in which the individual acts must have a minimum of stability.

We are not yet in a position even to conjecture what any of these minima might be; however, we can suggest that if the ego is indeed a complex of interconnected systems that are themselves systems of elements, then there cannot be any change in any egotized object or relationship or patterned event without disequilibrium of the system and some "ego sensation." This disequilibration should apply both to losses of cathected objects and additions of new objects—as in either case there must be some ego reorganization—and this in turn requires some dedifferentiation of sets so that there can be a rearticulation in a new organization. This concept of the ego suggests that there is a certain openness or vulnerability during such shifting because temporarily dedifferentiated sets cannot be mustered easily. The obvious example is loss of an important role partner,* but the formulation would suggest a temporary openness at such times as marriage or the advent of a child.

To elaborate upon the idea of loss of cathected objects, we might say that the ego loses stability because a "piece" is lost along with the object and must be reconstituted. Loose ends of

---

* Lindemann [4] points out that grief does not appear to be a function of the *kind* of affect felt for the deceased role partner but, rather, of the amount of interaction with him.

ideological and affective systems must also be tied up and reassigned, perhaps to new objects. Alternatively, some objects may lose meaning and require expulsion from the ego. For example, the death of a husband forces his widow to undertake both ego and environmental reorganization. If she has a child, she must realign herself to him in a two-person rather than in a three-person way, incorporating the memory of her husband as part of the culture of this two-person system. If her husband had been attached to his sister, his absence leaves the widow with a disruption of the ego organization that she had experienced as "my husband-and-his-sister." It is not surprising that we find empirically [5] that many widows, being older and with reduced cathexis, reorganize their lives by allowing the relationship with their husbands' relatives to die out.

On the other side of the coin, if the widow were to remarry, the incorporation of the new object and the multiplicity of slightly changed relationships that his presence would imply would also require ego reorganization.

To look at this process from the point of view of the environment, we might say that the organization of the ego depends for its effective function upon some kind of constancy of situation that can provide repeated confirmation to the ego sets used in dealing with it; that is, the environment must contain familiar objects, role constellations, and ideas. In stimulus-free environments, as we have noted, ego organization fails. When a child's environment is chronically impoverished, it seems likely that a reasonably well organized ego of little variety might result; this in turn might lead to a child's failure to adapt to major environmental changes, possibly because a child's whole ego structure, rather than just a portion of it, must dedifferentiate and disorganize in order to include new elements or compensate for the loss of old ones.*

---

* There probably are biological, neurological, and temperamental differences among people that influence the relative ease with which new

It is obvious that most ego shifts can be made quite easily by most people and that there is some compensating mechanism that allows stability to persist when elements of the ego are being dedifferentiated and rearticulated. Cases of extreme loss and crisis we shall discuss in the next chapter, as we advance our theory a little further. At present, we shall emphasize that the ego is thought of as in equilibrium but at the same time in a constant state of minor movement. That is, new experiences are constantly being encountered, cognized, sensed at the ego boundary, and interpreted and categorized in terms of existing sets. If there is no set or combination of sets available for comprehension of an experience, minor and possibly slow changes in organization may take place. New sets may indeed be developed before old ones are abandoned, and the dedifferentiation and rearticulation of the ego may correspond to such prosaic experiences as the "overlap" experienced in learning a new habit. Even though we know that the new car door opens differently from the old, we often revert to the old way that no longer works; but eventually, having incorporated the new way, we use it all the time. Such minor additions, subtractions, and rearrangements give the ego its almost protoplasmic aspect of flux and change.

Ego growth can be conceived of in similar terms. New experiences may require not only rearrangements but also the development of new sets. Furthermore, the manipulation of verbal symbols allows generalizations that can encompass many related sets and organizations at a higher level of abstraction than all of them. This kind of organization can then be used for developing still other new organizations to be tried out in future experiences. In this way, abstractions allow a kind of "set anticipation" and preparation for the future. Indeed, such

---

sets can be developed and incorporated into ego organization. We shall discuss differences in temperament in Chapter 4 when we deal with the problem of pathology.

general sets may be invoked specifically to envision a stable future at times of change and ego openness. The use of language for this process suggests that it is so important in the organization of the ego that the personality as we know it cannot develop without it. Furthermore, these generalizations allow the ego to free itself from the specifics of time or place. If difficulties arise, it is possible to anticipate relief; even in the normal course of events, this ability to transcend the immediate situation endows the ego with a core of autonomy.

To sum up: the constantly changing ego is, in a sense, a constantly open and potentially vulnerable ego; but this is its normal state. It must be in this condition in order to perform its functions. Moreover, the greater the variety of its ego sets and the greater its number of general ego organizations, the more buffered the ego is against the possibility of insult. Although this formulation may sound as if the ego were conceived to be in precarious equilibrium, it is really thought of as complex, flexible, and general—and able, through rearrangement and recombination of elements, to adapt successfully to a varied and changing environment. The ego is not ideally in equilibrium; it is ideally in motion—in a moving, steady state.

AFFECT

Because ego sets are in constant flux, the boundary of the ego must vary constantly. Therefore, both the condition of the environment and the level of organization of the ego will be reflected in affective responses. In general, coherent organizations should be accompanied by a pleasant affect and disorganizations by unpleasant sensations; and inasmuch as some motivation arises from tissue tensions, this unpleasant sensation may be a wellspring of the motivation to adapt—that is, to shift the ego organization or to modify the environment.

The interaction of the ego and the environment can result in a wide variety of affects. We assume, for example, that a sense of ego identity is generated when a well-organized ego, supported by adequate biological energy, acts in an appropriate environment. It is possible to imagine that a large number of familiar affective states can arise from the interaction between ego state and environment—as Table 1 suggests. In this table, the affects seem to range along dimensions of euphoria-dysphoria and stimulation-boredom. The former may be yielded by the interaction of the organized-disorganized aspects of ego and milieu and the latter by the "fit" between the variety and richness of ego sets and environmental elements. The table is, of course, speculative and intended only to suggest the variety of possible affects.

Table 1 seems to raise a question about ego identity. Erikson's original concept had three elements: first, it assumed a complex and coherent organization of elements; second, a reasonable harmony with the environment; and third, a confidence that this harmony would persist. Ego identity is thus defined as a harmonious relationship. The desirability of this relationship could rest, on the one hand, on the assumption that the environment is culturally valued and that the ego has adjusted to it. On the other hand, it could rest on the assumption that the manifestations of a complex, well-organized ego are valued and that therefore the environment has been brought into harmony with it. Erikson does not comment on the possibility of an underdeveloped ego being in harmony with an impoverished environment. The apathy of the patient on the chronic mental hospital ward must be thought of as a form of ego identity.*

Furthermore, since the time Erikson introduced the term "identity," others have used it in different ways—sometimes to mean little more than a firm self concept. Because of this, and

---

* This line of discussion raises the whole question of adaptation in extreme situations and converges on Bettelheim's [6] analyses of concentration camps.

TABLE 1

SOME AFFECTS GENERATED BY THE INTERACTION OF EGO AND ENVIRONMENT *

Condition of the Ego	Condition of Environment *			
	CLEARLY ORGANIZED		AMBIGUOUSLY ORGANIZED	
	Relatively Rich	*Relatively Impoverished*	*Relatively Rich*	*Relatively Impoverished*
ORGANIZED				
Many, well differentiated ego sets	Sense of appropriateness	Boredom	Intense curiosity	Mild curiosity
Few, but well differentiated ego sets	Sense of curiosity	Sense of appropriateness	Anxiety	Anxiety (Curiosity?)
DISORGANIZED				
Many, poorly differentiated ego sets	Sense of support	Frustration	Panic	Irritability
Few, poorly differentiated ego sets	Anxiety (Curiosity?)	Sense of support	Withdrawal	Apathy

* As the environment is not specified in any detail, these affects could all vary considerably. The table, however, points up the wide range of possible responses of different people to different kinds of milieu. It would not be anticipated that the content of the milieu could shift the affect into one of opposite tone. For example, the disorganized ego in an ambiguous milieu would be expected to experience negative or unpleasant affects; if the content of the milieu were changed, the affects might shift from irritability to withdrawal or panic but not to curiosity or a sense of support.

41

because of the assumption of a suitable environment that seems
to permeate the concept, we shall use it only in the way in
which we think Erikson meant it—that is, as a well-organized
ego acting in an appropriate environment with a sense of confidence in the persistence of both itself and the environment.*
However, we shall more often deal separately with its three
elements and discuss ego organization, the structure of the
milieu, and the expectation of future events.

SELECTION AND HIERARCHIZATION OF SETS

Not all ego sets are in use at once; not all are of the same
kind of usefulness. Some are concerned with action and some
with interpretation—both affective and cognitive. Both, of
course, can be used together in a variety of combinations and
grouped under a variety of generalizations. When a stimulus
requires interpretation or calls to action, different partial
organizations of the ego are brought into play either to interpret
the situation or to generate action. Sets are thus considered to
be relatively permanent aspects of ego organization, but they
may vary in strength or dominance according to the context
in which they were learned. By the same token they may have
hierarchical arrangements in terms of the cultural values surrounding their acquisition. In any situation these values may
influence the choice of action by invoking an appropriate hierarchical ordering of sets. This kind of hierarchy underlies all
manner of everyday behavior. Thus, we can be sitting and
thinking, totally concerned with inner events, and still instantly
shift our orientation to animated discussion if an unexpected
friend drops in. This rapid sorting process corresponds in our
terms with a complex and flexible ability to arrange or rearrange—or even refuse to rearrange—sets as the situation shifts.

---

* For a discussion of further problems with this complex idea, see
Jahoda's [7] discussion of "positive mental health."

The conception of hierarchical selections of sets, as indeed the whole conception of ego sets, leads again to the question of whether or not a translation into neurological terms is possible. However, such speculations are beyond our competence and the purpose of this book, and we shall not press them further.

EGO ABILITY

In general, ego ability can be called the capacity to find the sets or organizations to deal with any particular environmental problem and to hierarchize them appropriately to the problem. If, for example, a salesman must divide his weekends between his family and certain tasks connected with his work, the successful organization of uninterrupted periods for completing his tasks might be evidence of ego ability. However, putting the tasks aside and allowing attention and cathexis to flow onto sociable interaction is also evidence of ego ability.

The clinical term "ego strength," often used to indicate resistance to mental illness, we shall reserve to describe the general capacity of the ego—that is, the number and variety of sets, the generality and complexity of their organization, and the ability to hierarchize, select, and act out of appropriate organizations.

Ego organization can be thought of as being partly available to awareness through ego feeling and affective state and through the cognitive manner that we term "self concept." The average person asked to describe himself will present a list of physical descriptive attributes, a list of roles, and a list of general modes of acting. He might say, "I am a man, a mechanic, and an optimist." There is some evidence from the work of T. S. McPartland and John Cumming [8] that the reports will vary with ego state. The majority of the self-statements made by normal people are concerned with either status-role or style of social and personal interaction. These normal people seldom make the kind of concrete physical-descriptive statements that are found on drivers' licenses; similarly, they make very few abstruse personal statements that appear unrelated to status and role—such as, "I am a child of God." On admission to the hospital, schizophrenics do just the opposite. When asked to describe themselves, most of their statements either consist of unindividuated concrete labels, such as height or weight, or are abstruse personal statements; only a minority are anchored in social interaction. As they recover, the ratio of their statements changes until at discharge their lists of self-attributes resemble those of normal people. Inasmuch as identifying oneself realistically demands a measure of ego ability, the inability to do so is another example of ego failure.*

In summary, we have attempted in this chapter to regroup several familiar concepts into new ones: ego sets, ego organizations, and ego ability. We shall now return to the theme that bound Chapter 1 together—growth through crisis resolution—discuss some general concepts of crisis resolution, and rephrase them in our own terms so as to unify our theory.

---

* There is always the possibility that the subject may be perfectly well able to do the task but will refuse it for any of a variety of reasons; this, of course, is not ego failure in the sense that we mean it.

References

[1] ROBERT K. MERTON, "Continuities in the Theory of Reference Groups and Social Structure," *Social Theory and Social Structure*, 2nd ed. (Glencoe, Ill.: Free Press, 1957), p. 370.

[2] ANTHONY WALLACE, "Mazeway Disintegration: The Individual's Perception of Socio-Cultural Disorganization," *Human Organization*, XVI, 2 (1957), 23.

[3] E. VOLKHART (ed.), *Social Behavior and Personality*—Contributions of W. I. Thomas to Theory and Social Research (New York: Social Science Research Council, 1951).

[4] ERICH LINDEMANN, "Symptomatology and Management of Acute Grief," *American Journal of Psychiatry*, CI, 2 (1944), 141.

[5] ELAINE CUMMING and WILLIAM E. HENRY, *Growing Old* (New York: Basic Books, 1961), Ch. 8.

[6] BRUNO BETTELHEIM, *The Informed Heart* (New York: Harper, 1961).

[7] MARIE JAHODA, *Current Concepts of Positive Mental Health* (New York: Basic Books, 1958).

[8] T. S. McPARTLAND and JOHN CUMMING, "Self-Conception, Social Class, and Mental Health," *Human Organization*, XVII, 3 (1958), 24.

CHAPTER 3

Ego Growth
Through Crisis Resolution

In Chapter 1 we saw that a number of theories of ego formation rest upon an assumption that periodic disequilibriums between a developing child and his environment are followed by resolution and re-equilibrium at a higher level of ego organization. In this view, the normal development of a child is periodically marked by emergent biological changes that require a readaptation between him and the environment. Our extension of this concept suggests that, at each of these periods of openness and vulnerability, a successful resolution of the crisis enhances the ego by increasing the number and variety of sets and the complexity and generality of the organization. This brings ego organization into better harmony with the increasing demands of the environment and by the same token confirms the appropriateness of this organization when it is successfully invoked in handling that environment. In contrast, failure to resolve any developmental crisis leaves a child inadequately prepared to solve future ones because he has few or poorly differentiated sets and perhaps an inadequate level of organization.*

The phenomenon of interrupted equilibrium, however, is more general than this discussion has so far implied. We can distinguish three major types of disruptions, or life crises: the biologically tinged, the environmentally tinged, and the adventitious. We shall briefly discuss them here, not because we are centrally concerned with them but because they are important in the development of our theory and because we shall find familiar elements in them when we discuss the therapeutic milieu in operation.

The biologically tinged crisis can be thought of as completely inevitable, the environmentally tinged as somewhat less so, and the adventitious as not at all inevitable but occurring by chance with varying degrees of probability. Thus, the crises of growth are inevitable; the crises of retirement and loss of function with age are less so. Bereavement is less inevitable still, whereas personal disasters such as fire, flood, and war are basically chance events.

Growth, which we have discussed previously, is almost the prototype of the biologically tinged crisis. Illness is another biological crisis that has social and psychological overtones. Talcott Parsons and Renée Fox [2] have suggested that physical illness can, because of the way it is handled, result in a certain fluidity or vulnerability that can in turn result in change or growth.

We shall now discuss the interaction between ego and milieu associated with certain environmentally tinged crises.

---

* Caplan [1] and his co-workers have developed a theory of prevention of ego damage in children around the concepts of openness and vulnerability during crisis. As Caplan says: "A crisis situation involves both danger and opportunity."

RETIREMENT

Retirement from work is inevitable for most men and can be thought of as innate in the social life cycle if life goes on long enough. Furthermore, it is an anticipated change for which preparation can be made. Finally, as with epigenetic crises, it often occurs at a time of both physiological and psychological change. Elaine Cumming and William Henry, in *Growing Old,* have suggested that retirement differs in its dynamics from adolescent crises in only one important way: whereas the youth is acquiring more roles than he is losing, the aging person, at retirement, gives up more than he takes on. This requires reorganization of the open and vulnerable ego around fewer roles and objects and a shift in hierarchization so that sets related to action become less salient and sets related to meaning, interpretation, ideas, and values become more dominant. This reorganization is usually swift and successful for normal people.

MIGRATION OR CHANGE OF ENVIRONMENT

Of the environmentally tinged crises, migration lies next to retirement in inevitability. Like growth and retirement, migration—especially if it involves a change of culture—carries with it a temporary disruption of ego organization. Alfred Scheutz [3] points out that the stranger brings with him no history. His credentials must all be established anew, and aspects of his character that he has always taken for granted must be explicated. His concept of himself no longer receives automatic reinforcement from those who know such things as to whom he is kin, where he went to school, and the occupation of his wife's father. He must be overt, occasionally to the point of embarrassment, in setting forth his achievements, his avocations, his values, and his beliefs. In displaying them, he may for the first time examine their meaning himself. He finds himself in a minor crisis. If he maintains firm continuity with his past, it is difficult for him to mobilize ego sets appropriate for the new situation. Because of the resulting bad fit between himself and the environment, he will suffer feelings of ego diffusion. Furthermore, in order to act competently, he must overcome his nostalgia for old attachments sufficiently to become engaged with his new roles in his new environment. That is, he must be able to allow sufficient cathexis to flow to the new situation in order to perceive and interpret it correctly. In short, the migrant must undergo a temporary, and probably partial, ego disorganization while he acquires new sets, modifies some old ones, and rearranges the hierarchical ordering of the numerous sets involved in the losses and gains brought with the change. Some of the old attachments must be dealt with by the transmuting of the sets relating to them into ideational rather than interactive ego elements. As memories replace action, they must be assigned a different hierarchical position. In the meantime, the migrant must "educate" his environment to recognize his attributes. This double process is adaptation.* The ego is reorganized and the environment is modified, but many factors will determine which side of the process is dominant. It seems likely that the temperament and ability of the migrant will be influential, and that the role structure of the environment and his place in the structure will make a difference. In the ensuing chapters we shall discuss some of these questions in more detail.

It is through such a process of adaptation that a southerner must go when he moves north. He must interpret his "southern-ness" while he learns to conform to northern expectations. If he has successfully resolved crises in the past, he will be able

---

* Wechsler [4] has shown that the suicide and depression rates rise in communities of rapid in-migration, although the schizophrenia and alcoholism rates remain constant. This suggests a failure of adaptation in a certain type of person, and we shall return to his findings in Chapter 4.

to resolve this one. In fact, it is likely that with each successful resolution there will be an added stability to his ego that makes him less vulnerable, but at the same time less accessible, during crisis. This, of course, means that although he is less influenced by transient adversities, he would, by the same token, be less frequently open to change.

When we consider migration in these terms, it does not sound remarkably different from the problems encountered by a child experiencing biological growth and, along with it, the demand that he take on new roles and replace old objects with new ones.* The latter process differs from migration mainly in that a child is not severed from his history. It is reasonable to suppose, therefore, that migration is a crisis that, successfully resolved, results in ego growth or added complexity of ego organization.

GRIEF AND BEREAVEMENT

Grief and bereavement are environmentally tinged crises. Although they are not logically inevitable parts of life's experience, they are practically inescapable. Grief is probably more general and widespread than we are used to thinking. Whenever egotized objects are lost, grief is the appropriate affective response; hence, even migration involves the migrant in grief. Grief can be suffered following the loss of inanimate objects—houses, ships—that have come to symbolize the self or relationships with others. However, loss of an important role partner must, by its nature, result in a more intense grief— and possibly a qualitatively different grief—for here the loss is general and tends to diffuse through the whole ego because the lost person has been tied to so many sets and to so much of the

---

* We do not intend to imply that migration is a simple, well-understood phenomenon. It is a complex problem with an extensive literature of its own, but it is not central enough to our thesis to warrant extended treatment here.

environment. For this reason, the task of ego reconstitution is acute; the disrupted role relationship must be reconciled either by the substitution of someone else or by reorganization of the internal structure of the ego without it. Furthermore, the environment must be relearned without the important object. In spite of the inevitable loss, the ego can *sometimes* be both enriched and strengthened through the resolution of the bereavement crisis.* If the lost object is eventually replaced and the old object is incorporated symbolically, a wider variety of sets are available for organization, and the person is able to develop confidence in the persistence of his ability to handle future crises.† It may be such a feeling of confidence that lies behind the phrase, "Well, I've lived through *that*, so I think I could survive *anything.*"

Bereavement varies considerably in its degree of severity. The death of an aged person can result in less acute bereavement than the death of a young person.‡ This is because the aged, being relatively free from intense attachments and relatively peripheral to many of the role structures around them, do not create by their death severe ego problems for the survivors. Furthermore, their deaths are anticipated and "the work of mourning," as Freud [5] called it, is partly done ahead of time.

Grief, then, is an environmentally tinged crisis, variable

---

* This formulation has resonance with certain moral and religious dictums—blessed are the uses of adversity. We shall elaborate the point in a future publication.

† This in turn is part of the more general confidence in the persistent fit between the self and the environment that Erikson considers to be part of ego identity. It seems likely that in our terms this confidence is most closely connected to clear set differentiation, hence ability to select and hierarchize quickly, and hence an unimpaired sensing function at the ego boundary.

‡ A young newsman told one of us that when he covered obituaries he could guess the age of the deceased person by the amount of grief the survivors displayed over the telephone. The deaths of old people were benign compared to those of young people.

in its intensity, and therefore variable in its effect upon ego structure. When a young adult who is closely engaged with those around him dies suddenly, grief is severe, and a massive reconstitution of both the environment and the ego must be accomplished quickly. The speed is probably necessary because the whole ego is involved, and almost total dedifferentiation must take place before reorganization without the lost role partner can occur. During this phase the ego is extremely open, and action is difficult because appropriate sets cannot be mustered. Less severe grief, caused by loss of a peripheral role partner, can perhaps be encapsulated—fewer sets are involved —and restitution can take place over a longer period of time because action is still possible. Finally, minor losses, perhaps of things or even of cherished illusions, are probably remedied almost without notice. The unpleasant feeling of ego diffusion disappears as restitution takes place.

The third type of crisis, the adventitious, differs from the biologically and the environmentally tinged crises in being more various as well as less inevitable. However, because there are many kinds, a certain number of adventitious crises are likely to be encountered in every life cycle. Whenever the individual meets with serious disruptions and successfully overcomes them, he has resolved an adventitious crisis.

DISASTER

Of all the adventitious crises, disaster is the most severe, involving as it does the unexpectedness and arbitrariness of the event, multiple disruptions of the environment, and often multiple losses of objects with consequent bereavement and grief. In disaster, ego organization is most severely challenged, and the most general and immediate need of reorganization occurs. The crisis of disaster in this regard stands at the opposite pole from the epigenetic growth crisis, which is both gradual and adumbrated.

TRANSITION STATES

It is evident that there are elements common to all crises. When we turn to the empirical studies we find that Erich Lindemann,[6] James Tyhurst,[7] and others have noted a uniform pattern of response to crisis which seems almost invariant. In general, the first reaction is a psychological and physical turmoil, including aimless activity or immobilization and disturbances of body function, mood, mental content, and intellectual function. The second stage is characterized by a painful preoccupation with the past, and the third is a period of remobilization, activity, and adjustment. For example, Lindemann has pointed out that the newly bereaved person suffers a period of psychological and physiological turmoil that appears to be essential to the adequate discharge of his grief. All stages of response seem necessary for recovery, or ego reorganization. If any step is omitted, the prognosis must be guarded. Our theory would suggest that this is so for all crises. Although evidence of the order that Lindemann has presented is lacking, it could be predicted from our formulation that a chronic openness and vulnerability, a low level of set differentiation and organization, and a persistent sense of ego diffusion would accompany an unreconstituted ego insult. Furthermore, this condition of low differentiation would be accompanied by impaired ability to select and hierarchize sets and, hence, to act.

Tyhurst recognized a general pattern of response among normal people to what he called "transition states," and he spelled it out in detail for retirement, migration, and disaster. To these three he added bereavement and pointed out how grief, as formulated by Lindemann, could be viewed as a special case of transition, as well as an important ingredient of certain other transition crises.

Tyhurst's concept of the resolution of transition states is

analogous to a theory of the resolution of "hitches" developed
by William Ittelson and Hadley Cantril.[8] These authors, working experimentally with problems of cognition, conceive of
the individual as having an "assumptive state" regarding both
himself and the world. When this is questioned or fails to
work, there is a "hitch," or crisis, that requires him to redefine
either himself or the situation, or both. In numerous experiments, this group created hitches through the use of optical
illusions. They were then able to show that the subjects could
resolve the hitches if they were given small pieces of discrete
information. In our terms, the information represents new ego
elements that are either new sets or elements of several sets. The
new ego organization allows the environment to be redefined
in line with the assumptions—or, what is the same thing, the
assumptions to be brought into line with the environment. The
Cantril experiments become, in our terms, cognitive crises that
require minor ego reorganization for their solution.

At this point we must try to define the term "crisis" more
precisely. Following Tyhurst, we use it to refer to the impact
of any event that challenges the assumptive state and forces
the individual to change his view of, or readapt to, the world
or himself or both. When this occurs, it is likely that new combinations of established sets that have worked in the past will
be tried. If failure follows, either some dedifferentiation accompanied by diffusion feelings will ensue or a completely
new combination of sets will be mustered. If success is then
reached, a routine and minor ego organization has occurred
and identity feeling should be recovered. If new sets must be
developed, the crisis will last longer, the ego will be more
open to change, and reorganization may be at a slightly higher
level of generality.

In contrast to a crisis, a problem does not have to challenge the assumptive state. Although it has elements of
novelty, it can be solved by the use of new combinations of

available ego sets. No new types of role or object relationships need to be learned, nor do any loose ends of old relationships have to be accounted for.* A crisis, however, requires the learning of new sets and their integration into the ego, or the reorganization of the ego, following the loss of old sets. It is also possible that the whole ego may be involved in a crisis and not in problems.

Problem solution strengthens the ego by introducing new organizations of old sets and by the practice it provides—recall that it is assumed that ego organization must be used if it is to remain intact. However, successful crisis resolution results in ego growth because both new sets and organizations are thereafter available for use.

For any given person, it may be difficult to tell whether a particular event is experienced as a problem or as a crisis, but in general it is safe to say that the ego-damaged person will experience even simple problems as crises.

We have observed that crises are an intrinsic part of life and that certain patterned responses to them are adaptive even though they show clearly that the person is temporarily disequilibrated. Because of this, as Tyhurst has observed, the lifetime prevalence surveys of mental illness are basically meaningless. He was the first to point out that in times of transition adaptive behavior is similar to, and even identical with, behavior that would be called pathological were there no transition. In our terms, the normal person with a well-developed and well-organized ego will behave, when he is dealing with

---

* It seems to follow from this that people with well-organized, complex egos should experience more problems and fewer crises because they have a larger repertoire of sets. However, their very complexity may enable them to perceive more problematical situations and therefore experience more problems. Henry [9] in developing the idea of "affective complexity" has suggested that too wide a repertoire of affective alternatives in any situation may paralyze action. This would be congruent with our own formulation in Chapter 2 that a wide variety of sets with *poor organization* leads to anxiety in certain situations.

a crisis, in ways identical to the everyday behavior of a person with an inadequately developed ego.

We see, then, if our over-all formulation is correct, that ego growth is essentially a series of disequilibriums and subsequent re-equilibrations between the person and the environment.* Therefore, by extension, it seems reasonable that growth might be induced by presenting the individual with a series of graded crises under circumstances that maximize his chance of resolving them. *In other words, crisis resolution should be a therapeutic tool that can be scientifically controlled.* Thus, if an individual has been unable to solve problems because of inadequate biological endowment or extreme environmental stress, he should experience ego growth and reorganization if he is introduced to carefully controlled minor crises in a protected situation.

Crisis resolution, then, promotes ego growth by increasing the repertoire of ego sets and possibly by increasing the differentiation of the sets. This increases the generality of the organization—because it is unlikely that general organizations of sets will occur if the sets themselves are poorly defined. The reaffirmation of the utility of the sets, in turn, can be expected to sharpen their differentiation and strengthen the organization. This, in turn, will allow a sharp sensing function at the ego boundary, a clear perception and adequate interpretation of the environment, and, together with the wide repertoire of sets, confidence in the ability to continue to cope with it. Such confidence will be reflected in willingness to tackle new or problematical situations, and the ego growth pattern can then be repeated. At some point, what may be thought of as the *mature ego* can be expected to reach a stable plateau with a

---

* In a sense, this concept of interplay between the demands of the environment and the capacity of the individual resembles Freud's concept of the conflict-born ego.

rather low recognition of crisis and infrequent openness to change.

In summary, we have developed a formulation about the development and function of the ego in terms of its environment. We have done this in order to return to a consideration of the therapeutic milieu as we defined it: "the scientific manipulation of the environment aimed at producing changes in the personality of the patient." The milieu is specifically built around the introduction of controlled crises in a protected situation. In the next chapter, we shall discuss in more detail the types of ego damage which we might expect to treat in this way and we shall set forth the basic general specifications of that milieu.

References

[1] GERALD CAPLAN (ed.), *Prevention of Mental Disorders in Children: Initial Explorations* (New York: Basic Books, 1961).

[2] TALCOTT PARSONS and RENÉE C. FOX, "Illness, Therapy and the Modern Urban American Family," *Journal of Social Issues*, VIII, 4 (1952), 31.

[3] ALFRED SCHEUTZ, "The Stranger: An Essay in Social Psychology," *American Journal of Sociology*, XLIX, 6 (May 1944), 499.

[4] HENRY WECHSLER, "Community Growth, Depressive Disorders, and Suicide," *The American Journal of Sociology*, LXVII, 1 (1961), 9.

[5] SIGMUND FREUD, "Mourning and Melancholia," *The Complete Psychological Works of Sigmund Freud,* standard ed., Vol. 14 (London: Hogarth Press, 1957), 243-260.

[6] ERICH LINDEMANN, "Symptomatology and Management of Acute Grief," *American Journal of Psychiatry*, CI, 2 (1944), 141.

[7] JAMES TYHURST, "The Role of Transition States—Including Disasters—In Mental Illness," *The Walter Reed Symposium on Preventive and Social Psychiatry* (Washington, D.C.: Government Printing Office, 1958).

[8] WILLIAM H. ITTELSON and HADLEY CANTRIL, *Perception. A Transactional Approach* (New York: Doubleday, 1954).

[9] WILLIAM E. HENRY, "Affective Complexity and Role Perceptions: Some Suggestions for a Conceptual Framework for the Study of Adult Personality," in John E. Anderson (ed.), *Psychological Aspects of Aging* (Washington, D.C.: American Psychological Association, 1956).

CHAPTER 4

The General Characteristics
of the Patients and the Milieu

In this chapter, in order to bring our formulations into the realm of clinical familiarity, we shall suggest how a set of categories developed in terms of ego damage can articulate with some conventional psychiatric categories. We shall then suggest the bare outlines of the therapeutic milieu.

I. The Characteristics of the Patients

Any damage to the ego must affect both the executive and the synthetic functions because of the interdependent relationship between them. For our purposes, executive failure is the focus of interest because it is through providing problems for the patient to solve that the milieu exercises its primary therapeutic influence. Nevertheless, the synthetic function is always involved, and it should be borne in mind that the subsequent discussion deliberately omits extensive consideration of impulse control, guilt, and so on in favor of discussing executive failures. In one sense, our theory is complementary to those underlying the dyadic therapies. These are performed under strictly controlled circumstances in which the therapist lays out the ground rules and the patient agrees to abide by them. For this reason, such therapies can deal directly with the synthetic function and the unconscious material that inevitably becomes involved. Finally, this type of therapy can meet the issue of drive and impulse control directly, because the rules of the therapy help maintain control of the patient. Milieu therapy, however, takes place in circumstances in which much control is vested, as it is in everyday life, in the primary group and is, therefore, exercised by both patients and staff members over one another. Such a therapy must grapple with the practical manifestations of damage to executive function. Because the milieu is more lifelike than the controlled two-person relationship and because it is assumed that synthetic function can be improved through executive function channels, we would argue that milieu therapy is as effective as dyadic therapy and more easily generalized to the total life situation.

Before discussing traditional diagnostic categories in terms of ego damage, we should like to suggest that differences in temperament—that is, innate, biologically based differences—inevitably influence the way in which ego failure is manifested.

We make a slightly different use of the traditional concept of temperament. We shall use the terms "impingers" and "selectors" to refer to extreme extroverts and extreme introverts. We have chosen these terms to express as nearly as possible the effects on ego function and interaction of the two temperamental extremes.

The impinger, in this scheme, generates inferences about himself, tries them out on the environment, and learns the nature both of the environment and of himself by watching the reactions of others. If the reflections of his cues are out of keeping with his ego organization, he will try to change the environment. Only if he fails will he reorganize his assumptive state in order to adapt. The selector, on the other hand, tends to insinuate himself into the environment in order to derive an image of himself from the ongoing flow of cues. It is only when he fails to find confirmatory cues that he will adapt through ego reorganization.

The more extreme the impinger, the harder he will try to change the environment before adapting; the more extreme the selector, the longer he will remain withdrawn, waiting for suitable cues, before adapting.

We assume that temperamental types are normally distributed in the population like any other multidetermined, biologically based characteristic and that few people have these extreme temperaments. We assume that the modal person can both impinge and select as the occasion demands, although some people will be noticeably more likely to impinge and others to select. However, these will still be able to shift to the alternate pattern.* If they have no other complicating ego problems, people probably can be fairly extreme selectors or impingers and can be known as "shy" or "wise" on the one hand and "tempermental" or a "ball of fire" on the other. The extreme types probably will have systematically different ego feelings and will experience the world differently.

Keeping in mind that most people can perform both of these operations, and that only extreme temperaments can confound diagnoses, we shall return to a brief general consideration of four possible kinds of ego damage. The first two are primarily inadequacies of ego development; the next two are primarily failures of ego ability.

---

* This sounds as if set hierarchization were at issue, but we mean to refer only to a biological predisposition toward one mode or the other. Undoubtedly ego ability will confuse the picture in any concrete case. It is quite possible, too, that proneness to loss of hierarchies is partly dependent on temperament.

TOO FEW EGO SETS AS A PRIMARY
EGO INADEQUACY

The ordinary mental defective, lacking in biological en-dowment, is the prototype of uncomplicated ego poverty. His ego organization may be adequate, but his capacity to handle complicated environmental problems, especially if they require general sets, is lacking. The simple defective is thought of as having a modal temperament, and this will probably allow him to be recognized early as a defective and socialized to that role. If he is an impinger or a selector he will probably be defined differently. There is evidence [1] that the repeated use in the therapeutic milieu of such ego function as the defective has is the ideal treatment.

Ego poverty can result from neglect and isolation in child-hood—a low level of interaction leading in extreme cases to the so-called "feral" condition. The few known cases (see Davis, "Final Note on a Case of Extreme Isolation," p. 432) indicate that social retraining is possible.

Some ego poverty results from the loss of sets acquired at an earlier time. Traumatic injuries, cerebrovascular accidents, brain tumors, arteriosclerotic brain disease, and Korsakoff's syndrome are all disorders in which this may have occurred. These patients sometimes find that others do not comprehend the extent of their problem and therefore try to pretend that nothing has happened. But if they cannot handle the environ-ment skillfully, this maneuver cuts them off from help in re-learning. They are then driven to fill in the gaps in their com-petency by inventions; this can result in overactivity, confabu-lation, and other symptoms,* often exacerbated by the fact that people around them accept their often quite serious physical

---

* These patients can also develop depressions in a mechanism similar to that described later for reactive depressions.

disabilities but expect them to behave socially as normal adults. Some of these manifestations have been described by Edwin Weinstein, Robert Kahn, and Sidney Malitz [2] as socially induced secondary symptoms in brain damage.

A similar problem can be created for the brain-damaged patient by people who, with the best of intentions, "humor" them with helpful untruths. This process creates environmental ambiguity and confounds the patient's problems by introducing further doubts of his own ability to perceive accurately. This in turn leads to diffusion feelings and lack of confidence.

Some ego set poverty is complicated by weak differentiation of sets, consequent inability to select sets, and, perhaps, spreading of excitation to inappropriate channels. Spreading of excitation is difficult to separate conceptually from weak differentiation of sets. Spreading is a pathological way of handling incoming stimuli. Responses to some stimuli seem so highly charged or so anxiety laden that instead of involving an appropriate ego organization they overflow, color the whole ego, distort interpretation, and weaken impulse control. The effect is analagous to the spread of excitation from a focus in epilepsy. Indeed, migraine, which is characterized by cerebral dysrhythmia, shows a prodromal irritability that suggests spreading. In the first case, spreading seems to be the result of synthetic function failure; in the second, it is associated with manifest organic malfunction. We group them under a single term for they seem to have a similar final reaction pattern.

Lack of differentiation and spreading, in addition to set poverty, will result in the blurring of ego boundary sensations and, hence, diffusion feeling with its spectrum of negative affect. In such cases, some secondary ego disorganization and failure of set hierarchization is almost inevitable because the relationship among the sets is unclear; complex, well-organized, and general sets are therefore impossible.

Such ego damage can probably take place in several ways. Early brain damage might produce a neurological picture predisposed toward spreading. Socialization by people with ambiguous roles or under conditions of obscure or ambiguous communication might prevent the necessary minimum differentiation of sets from taking place.

It has long been thought that in physical retraining undamaged portions of the brain can compensate for the areas lost by tissue damage. This principle has been little used for social retraining until a few experiments with milieu therapy showed its potential value. Special techniques of retraining, and drugs to control spreading, are probably necessary as part of the treatment in all such cases.

A final example of ego impoverishment is the so-called process schizophrenic. In these patients the picture is confused by an extreme selector temperament. These patients appear to be consistently unable to affirm their ego organizations and assumptive states in interaction and therefore turn to fantasy as a substitute.* Eventually they become entirely dependent upon an environment with which they have almost no contact. They may suffer not so much from absolute set poverty but rather from an efflorescence of sets and organizations concerned with symbols, affects, and inner stimuli combined with a relative poverty of sets concerned with action, apperception, and cognition. A study of first admissions of male schizophrenics to a state hospital [3] has revealed a homogeneous group of young inadequate patients, many of whom have never worked and whose symptoms have been of long duration. The hospitalization of these patients seems to have come about only when the family that had been supporting them disintegrated. Such pa-

---

* For a comprehensive discussion of schizophrenia from a similar point of view, see the work of Shakow.[4]

tients no doubt suffer from secondary ego disabilities, but the primary pathology appears to be set poverty in an extreme selector temperament.

POOR DIFFERENTIATION AND SPREADING AS A PRIMARY INADEQUACY

Under this heading we have grouped both the acute reactive schizophrenic and those chronic schizophrenics who are not suffering from primary set poverty. The reactive schizophrenic suffers from a drastic ego disorganization as well as poor differentiation and spreading. His distorted use of symbols may result from an inability to muster appropriate sets and organizations. His periods of apparent low energy may also be connected with his complete inability to choose among a number of poorly differentiated sets and his inability to resolve the ambiguities and anxiety generated by his poor fit with the situation.*

The chronic schizophrenic differs from the acute in having secondary loss of ego sets. This is caused by his withdrawal and by the impoverishment of the environment. The ego, through disuse, is further weakened by a circular process; and spreading, with its resulting confusion, makes it impossible to find appropriate channels for unacceptable impulses. In this sense, spreading is empirically inseparable from synthetic function failure.

Some schizophrenic behavior has been thought of as inappropriately concrete and some as manifesting an ego boundary failure. Freeman, Cameron, and McGhie, in *Chronic Schizophrenia*, give an example of the latter in their description of a schizophrenic girl who could not discriminate be-

---

* This should probably not be confused with hierarchization failure. The latter is an inability to make some sets come into salience and others remain latent in a way appropriate to the situation. But there need be no lack of differentiation.

tween herself and someone wearing her coat, presumably because she felt it to be part of herself. In our terms, the girl had
selected an inappropriate ego organization for distinguishing
among people. To establish identity by the clothes being worn
reflects, in our view, a total failure of set selection. Her technique is no more concrete, of course, than the conventional
way of identifying people through features, hair color, and
build, but it is culturally inappropriate. In our opinion she
does not necessarily have a difficulty in self-identification and
ego boundary, although she might.

The first task of the milieu is to resolve acute ego disorganization, and we shall describe the process in Chapter 10.
After this, the milieu must assist the patient to develop more
strongly entrenched, better differentiated sets that lead to a
more culturally acceptable use of symbols and choices of generalization and abstraction.

FAILURE OF HIERARCHIZATION AS THE
PRIMARY EGO DISABILITY

This category includes the reactive depressions and the
neuroses; psychotic depressions appear to be complicated by
a tendency toward spreading—a developmental failure.

Ego ability refers to the ability to muster appropriate ego
organizations. Inappropriate organizations must at the same
time be held latent. However, it seems probable that when
strongly entrenched and differentiated sets are held latent,
there must be a confidence that they will be usable at some
future time.* In the normal person it is probably possible

---

* It seems possible that sets can be kept latent for long periods of
time without being lost if there is a certain amount of anticipation of
their use. This may be one of the differences between the deteriorated
schizophrenic in an impoverished environment and an undeteriorated
criminal in solitary confinement—the confidence that the ego will again
be able to come into full play.

to project into the future an image of the self using the temporarily latent organizations; anticipation may, in fact, have a reinforcing effect similar to actual use.

The inability to hierarchize in this manner may be the basis of neuroses in which inappropriate ego organizations are repeatedly used in spite of their lack of utility. This is not an inability to choose organizations, such as schizophrenics may suffer, but an inability to muster them or, alternately, an inability to hold them latent.* The neuroses, of course, have been fully explored in terms of synthetic function failures and the defense mechanisms mobilized against them. One of the characteristics of these disorders is the involvement of symbolic behavior in the inappropriate responses and a consequent hypersensitivity to symbols.

Temperament probably influences the way in which symptoms are expressed. Those with selector temperaments should, in this scheme, be most likely to display anxiety as the situation becomes less and less appropriate to their ego organization and the ability to reorganize is lacking. Impinger temperaments would be expected to react with depression. The depressions associated with bereavement or retirement can be formulated as follows: The individual finds himself in a disrupted and de-differentiated system, and his problem can only be solved by ego reorganization because the situation simply cannot be changed. Nevertheless, because of his temperament he persists in his attempts to change the situation. Failure increases his diffusion feelings and distressed affects. Furthermore, his failure to confirm his ego organization reaches into the future because he cannot project himself in a changed state, and he cannot project an unchanged situation because he *knows* it has changed. This results in a sense of powerlessness in dealing

---

* The inappropriate strong response is often related to situations in which it was learned in early life. Therefore, the metaphor of regression is often used to explain it.

with the environment and a sense of hopelessness about the future. He experiences the poor fit between himself and the world as personal inadequacy because his habitual way of solving problems is to change the environment. By this kind of reasoning, our scheme is in harmony with Edward Bibring's formulation (see "The Mechanism of Depression") that depression is born in a conflict between aspiration and capability.

For the neurotic in psychotherapy, insight and the "working through" of the transference may be thought of as the modification of such strong anachronistic organizations to make them appropriate to the present problems. Some psychoanalysts such as Allen Wheelis [5] have emphasized that character change depends on insight being put to use in a social context. Although this book is not focused on the treatment of the psychoneurotic, it is probable that its approach could be adapted to this task, especially as there is reason to suppose, from the work of Ian Stevenson and others,[6] that ego reorganization in neurotics can take place through accidents and other fortuitous events. In addition, Michael Shepherd and E. M. Gruenberg [7] have reported that untreated neuroses seem to last, on the average, only about two years. Although this kind of evidence suggests that the neurotic is amenable to environmentally induced ego changes, the relationship of our theory to neurotic disorders is not yet worked out in any detail.

If failure of ego ability is accompanied by a tendency to poor set differentiation, the result will be spreading, a blurred cognitive picture, ambiguous interpretations of stimuli, and, in general, the impaired contact with reality that characterizes the psychotic depression. Temperament might also be a complicating factor in such cases. We might hypothesize that the psychotic depression is basically a neurotic depression with spreading.

If the slowing or immobilization of the depressed person persists over a long time, his ego sets will be weakened from disuse. In fact, Silvano Arieti [8] has described manic-depressive patients who, after many years in mental hospitals, have been reclassified as schizophrenics because their symptom pattern changed during their years in hospital.

ACUTE EGO DISORGANIZATION

Under certain disastrous environmental conditions, ego ability can fail completely, and the resulting acute loss of ego organization can manifest itself in stuporous states or meaningless overactive behavior. Disorganizations produced by environmental breakdown can be treated rapidly and successfully in a highly structured milieu, and there is a great amount of literature on disaster that confirms this. If the patient is not removed from the disaster area, his ability to reorganize will be slowed because the situational disorganization will reinforce his own.

There is a possibility that such vague conditions as "neurasthenia" and "low psychic energy" can be better described as low grade and chronic ego disorganization, perhaps with low biological energy.

In concluding this speculation we should point out that our scheme does not at this point include a concept of psychopathy or character disorder. The psychopath is generally thought to have a disordered superego and to be resistant to treatment. Maxwell Jones,[9] however, has had some success in treating such patients. He places them in a milieu in which every antisocial act is subject to discussion and sanction by the whole therapeutic community. The patients are under constant observation and, therefore, the control of their peers and the staff. Eventually some of them seem to learn how to behave in a more acceptable way. This may be because the deficient superego is bolstered by improved ego function, and even if the patient cannot use the norms and values as inner guides, he can at least discern other people's responses to his behavior.

Harry Wilmer [10] has reported success in using Jones' method with both neurotic and psychotic patients, but, in general, the therapeutic community has not had widespread use, and replicating Jones' type of therapeutic community would be helpful.

Although this discussion of pathology is incomplete, it bears a working relationship to the kinds of things that can be done for patients to restore them to society as functioning members. Furthermore, it should eventually be possible to articulate it to biological and neurophysiological theories on the one hand and to establish more precise connections with social-structural theories on the other.

II.   The Characteristics of the Milieu

Ego restitution may involve reorganization, redifferentiation, restitution of lost sets, addition of new sets, or set re-hierarchization. In order to enable these things to happen, the milieu must offer to the patient a clear, organized, and unambiguous social structure, problems to solve in protected situations, and a variety of settings in which to solve these problems.* It should also offer him a peer group and a helpful staff to encourage and assist him to live more effectively. The program should aim at equipping the patient to act in clearly defined roles powered by a variety of motivating forces and governed by different cultural values. This should ideally result in an ego structure sufficiently differentiated and varied to allow a wide range of competence. No single disequilibrating event should then be able to disorder the patient's whole ego structure. In a sense, the treatment should prevent the patient from being bound to any particular event or any particular moment in time. This protects him from diffusion of ego feeling, loss of confidence, and paralysis of choice. At this point we have techniques to produce such happy results with only a

---

* Many details of the *content* of problems will be offered in the second and third parts of this book.

fraction of our patients, but virtually all can to some degree be improved.

A paradox must first be faced in establishing such a milieu. The situation must initially be structured so as to lower anxiety because anxiety interferes with learning and problem solution, but at the same time it must present the patient with the task of problem solution—in itself anxiety producing. Because seriously ill patients can tolerate only limited amounts of anxiety without further ego disorganization, particular pains must be taken to shelter the acutely ill patient from *gratuitous* sources of anxiety.

There is an important reservation to this basic rule, however. The patient must eventually return to the normal amount of anxiety of the outside world or, if he is being treated in a clinic, he must face this anxiety every day. For this reason the control of gratuitous anxiety must always be a temporary measure used to allow the most acutely ill patients to begin ego restitution, and from the start they must be aware of this.

A healthy individual is expected to be able to solve a wide variety of problems in a large number of settings, among which, in our society, the two most important are family and work. The solution of problems in these two areas, however, requires the successful assumption of appropriate roles. Recreation and voluntary association with others for common ends are often considered important, but it is only when problems are not solved in the first two areas that general personal failure is socially recognized. A man may be "unable to relax and play" or he may "give nothing to the community" and still be considered adequate and normal, but if he fails to provide a living, he is in trouble. The same applies to a married woman's maintenance of an adequate household and an atmosphere of reasonable tranquillity.

We have no way of talking about roles that is exactly coordinate with the way we have talked about ego function and problem solution. Therefore, we shall follow Parsons [11] and Bales [12] and discuss this division of labor in terms of adaptive or instrumental roles oriented to grappling with the environment, and integrative or socio-emotional roles concerned with relationships among people. Everyone must be able to move from one type of role to the other, as the situation demands, but, generally speaking, men tend to stand between women and the world of work and women to stand between men and the world of sociability. This goes further than men earning the living and women maintaining an atmosphere in which men can daily reconstitute their motivation. Even when women work, there is a tendency for men to "advise" them regarding such instrumental matters as investments, and even though men may be occupied in positions demanding socio-emotional interaction, there is a tendency, when men and women are together, for women to take on the tension-lowering, sociability role and the men to take on instrumental, goal-directed activity.* Fred Strodtbeck and Richard Mann [13] have shown how this occurs even among jury members who, presumably, had all been given identical roles to start with.

These instrumental and integrative roles appear to involve different ego organizations. For example, it seems plausible to believe that a marked difference in ego feeling results from acting in these two different kinds of roles. Observing a person engaged in goal-directed activity, we see concentration or fixed attention. At the same time ego feeling may "flow to one place" as if a pseudopod of concentrated awareness had been put out. At this time other ego organizations and their feelings are faint and far from awareness. The ability to hierarchize may be essential to this activity.

---

* Obviously, when women are alone with children or meeting with other women, they must assume instrumental leadership, just as when men are alone some of them must play socio-emotional roles. See Bales [12] on this point.

During socio-emotional acts, ego organization may be more generalized and dispersed in order for tension to be sensed. The greater the number of people involved, the more generalized and abstract must be the organization so that all can be "kept track of" no matter how they differ. This dispersion of ego feeling may require firm set differentiation in order for organization to be maintained. Furthermore, if it is necessary to combine this kind of role activity with certain instrumental duties, the alternation may generate characteristic types of fatigue. Wanting to "get away from it all" is said, by some, to be a characteristically feminine desire; nevertheless, it may be that certain role prescriptions are harder to carry out than others, and men employed in positions requiring them to reconcile differences among people and yet take instrumental responsibilities may, like women, be acting in intrinsically difficult roles.

Even if there are predispositions to fail in certain types of roles because of temperament, ego characteristics, or situational factors, all types of roles must be understood before there can be effective social interaction. For this reason the milieu must provide opportunities to improve role performance in areas of past failure and also opportunities to interact in situations where new kinds of roles are being played.*

At the practical level, some roles are more vital than others. More particularly, men must usually earn a living, and instrumental competence is therefore vital for them. Theoretically, we would expect the socio-emotional role to be vital for women—and for maintenance of a balance in the home, it may well be. However, recent studies of John Cumming, Leo Miller, and Isabel McCaffrey [14] suggest that women are hospitalized only when they fail in the more *instrumental* tasks of

---

* This also allows the patient to develop a repertoire of ego organizations that keep him from being disorganized by minor failures. They are a reserve of capacities in which he can have confidence.

the home—housework and child care. The socio-emotional role seems so essential to the integrity of social life and, at the same time, so vaguely defined in our culture that if a married woman fails in it, her husband may be able to take on certain aspects of it. Only if she fails in the instrumental aspects and does not have a mother or sisters available to help with them is she likely to reach a mental hospital. Let us emphasize, however, that, as far as we know, ability to perform the instrumental aspect of the mother-wife role serves only to prevent hospitalization. In the end a wife's socio-emotional failure, although it may not lead to hospitalization, may totally disrupt the marriage.

This discussion of role demands suggests that failure to solve certain problems presented by these roles is related to ego damage. It should, then, be possible to think of patients both in terms of their symptoms and of the milieu in which they will have to operate. For example, in a hospital setting occupational retraining may be a paramount need of some men, repeated practice at goal-directed decision making may be the central therapy for others, and the reaching of a consensus about a group problem may be the most important ego-strengthening process for some women.

Finally, the chief gain for some people may lie in their becoming able to react appropriately to a variety of situations rather than excelling in a narrow area, no matter how appropriate the latter situation may be to their central role. This gain would allow them to experience small failures without involving their total life situation. For these people, a number of memberships in different groups, with separate social anchorages and distinctive labels, may be protective.

We see then that the milieu must provide the patients with practice in the kinds of role behavior that will be expected of them as participating members of society and, at the same time, provide them with a range of problems for solution. These problems may vary in accord with the patients' disorders.

For example, it seems reasonable that set differentiation might be enhanced by problem solution in unambiguously separate situations, that failure of hierarchization might in part be treated by a series of graded problems centered upon planning for future changes, and that poverty of ego sets might be helped by simple cognitive learning.

Not only will theory help to suggest methods for treating patients, but the accumulated empirical wisdom of those who have handled them for a number of years will enrich the program. It is a commonplace that the best predictors of patients' progress outside the hospital are the ward personnel. By the same token, the know-how of ward personnel can be built into treatment programs and their knowledge of what constitutes a problem exploited.

For the solution of these various types of problems, the milieu must provide information, facilities, support, considerable freedom of action, and protection against too severe consequences of failure. All this requires adequate physical settings, sufficient supplies, and a social structure whose policy is made and executed in the interests of the therapeutic milieu. Most important, many of the problems must be solved in groups in which everyone has full membership. In this way new ego organizations are learned in lifelike situations involving a full range of ego activity.

Besides problems to solve and an appropriate climate in which to solve them, the milieu must contain helpful people who are rooted in the nondeviant world.* Staff members of treatment centers must have roles that allow them to reintroduce the patient to culturally acceptable ways of behaving and, at the same time, allow them to recognize wide variations in acceptable patterns. It is not possible, in this view, for a staff member to participate in a therapeutic environment

---

* For a detailed description of this concept see Parsons, *The Social System,* Ch. VII.

without being part of a subsociety with his patients. If the staff member is not part of this subsociety, his patients cannot egotize him and strengthen their own organizations in repeated social interaction with him. But if the staff member does take on membership, it has to be moral and normative, because *no* social system can operate without norms, rules, and culture.* Interaction creates sentiments between people and these sentiments become the norms of the interaction. For this reason staff members must represent the nondeviant culture, although their training must enable them to tolerate deviant behavior as a *temporary* state and, when necessary, to make sense of a patient's apparently senseless behavior. Finally, just as a parent is only effective as a socializing agent if he has available a wider repertoire of roles than his child, so a therapeutic agent is only effective if he has a wider variety of functioning roles and correspondingly more sets and more coherent ego organizations than his patient. If, for example, a hospital ward is run by attendants who do not take their work seriously, male patients will find it hard to relearn a commitment to the world of work. While the attendant is caring for the patient he is doing his daily work, and the patient, gratuitously, is learning, through taking the role of the other, his attitudes toward it.

We shall now turn to the practical aspects of the milieu, and in the five chapters of Part II we shall elaborate its structure in detail. In Part III we shall describe the programs of action within the milieu that we have shown to be therapeutic or that we can predict, from our earlier formulations, should be therapeutic.

---

* This sounds similar to the moral treatment of the 19th century. We believe it is, and one of the tasks of the theory of milieu therapy is the codification and verification of moral treatment.

References

[1] N. O'CONNOR and J. TIZARD, *The Social Problem of Mental Deficiency* (London: Methuen, 1958).

[2] EDWIN A. WEINSTEIN, ROBERT KAHN, and SIDNEY MALITZ, "Confabulation as a Social Process," *Psychiatry*, XIX, 4 (1956), 383.

[3] JOHN CUMMING and LEO MILLER, "Isolation, Family Structure, and Schizophrenia" (paper read to the World Congress of Psychiatry, Montreal, Canada, June 1961).

[4] DAVID SHAKOW, "Segmental Set, A Theory of the Formal Psychological Deficit in Schizophrenia," A.M.A. *Archives of General Psychiatry*, 6 (January 1962), 1.

[5] ALLEN WHEELIS, "Will and Psychoanalysis," *Journal of American Psychoanalytic Association*, 4 (1956), 285.

[6] IAN STEVENSON, "Processes of Spontaneous Recovery from the Psychoneuroses," *American Journal of Psychiatry*, 117, 12 (1961), 1057; GEORGE SASLOW and ANN D. PETERS, "A Follow-up Study of 'Untreated' Patients with Various Behavior Disorders," *Psychiatric Quarterly*, 30 (1956).

[7] MICHAEL SHEPHERD and E. M. GRUENBERG, "The Age for Neuroses," *The Milbank Memorial Fund Quarterly*, XXXV, 3 (July 1957).

[8] SILVANO ARIETI, "Manic-Depressive Psychosis," *American Handbook of Psychiatry*, 1 (New York: Basic Books, 1959), 419.

[9] MAXWELL JONES, *Social Psychiatry* (London: Tavistock Publications, 1952).

[10] HARRY WILMER, *Social Psychiatry in Action* (Springfield, Ill.: Charles C. Thomas, 1958).

[11] TALCOTT PARSONS, *The Social System* (Glencoe, Ill.: Free Press, 1951).

[12] ROBERT F. BALES, "The Equilibrium Problem in Small Groups," *Working Papers in the Theory of Action* (Glencoe, Ill.: Free Press, 1953), Ch. V.

[13] FRED STRODTBECK and RICHARD D. MANN, "Sex Role Differentiation in Jury Deliberations," *Sociometry*, XIX, 1 (March 1956), 3.

[14] JOHN CUMMING, LEO MILLER, and ISABEL McCAFFREY, "Studies in Family Structure and Schizophrenia" (unpublished manuscripts).

PART II

THE STRUCTURE
OF THE MILIEU

Introduction to Part II

This section of five chapters offers a change of pace. It can be looked upon as illustration of the theory or as application, depending upon the point of view. In it we shall construct from sociological theory and from practical experience some specifications for the ideal therapeutic milieu. The concrete, specific, and sometimes pedestrian aspects will be discussed—often anecdotally—with special reference to the mental hospital. We shall be interested in ego restitution, but we shall emphasize the return of normal social function. In the words of a World Health Organization Committee report:

> All approaches . . . lead to the conclusion that mental illness causes a loss of adaptability and integration with the environment, and this loss leads to a return to more primitive ways of functioning. Treatment for psychiatric illness is aimed not only at the removal of symptoms, *but also the provision of facilities that will enable the patient once again to develop his relationship with his environment.* [Italics ours.] [1]

This Part will relate the milieu to the concepts of ego damage and ego restitution, but the emphasis will center upon the practical task of specifying the structure of the therapeutic milieu. Following this, the chapters of Part III will discuss some of the day-to-day functioning of the therapeutic environment and will try to give some of the flavor of a program in action. We shall also discuss in some detail the potentiality for therapeutic environments in the community.

Many of the examples used throughout this part and the next are taken from the two hospitals with which the authors have had more prolonged experience. The first was the Saskatchewan Hospital in Weyburn, Saskatchewan, a 2,000-bedded public mental hospital in which we both worked in 1954 and 1955.* The second was the Kansas City Receiving Center, a 70-bedded psychiatric hospital admitting the acutely mentally ill from Kansas City; John Cumming was associated with it in 1956 and 1957.† Some examples will be drawn from clinics, day hospitals, and hospitals of which we have less complete knowledge.

At this point we enter a caveat about the ensuing chapters. There is wide variation among hospitals; not all readers will be familiar with the full range. Some people who have read this book in manuscript think that we describe situations so archaic that sophisticated readers will be alienated. Others feel that we assume so much progress in the care and treatment of the mentally ill that the state hospital psychiatrist might put the book aside as irrelevant to his conditions of work. We believe that all the therapeutic practices described here can be modified for the situation in any hospital. Furthermore, all the illustrations of ego-damaging practices can be found in many hospitals today.

When we joined Weyburn Hospital's staff, it was a typical,

---

* John Cumming was Senior Psychiatrist with responsibility for 900 male patients, and Elaine Cumming was Special Assistant to the Clinical Director.

† John Cumming was Director of Outpatient Services and Research; Elaine Cumming was not associated with this hospital.

large, physically isolated state hospital with a high proportion of degraded, chronic patients and a reasonably active and attractive admissions unit. As with most hospitals of its kind, it had a traditional, rigidly hierarchical social structure with little communication among the various departments. Doctors had little authority, and the business manager and his staff, together with the chief attendant and the head nurse, effectively controlled much of what went on in the hospital. Visitors to the wards of such hospitals always notice first the silence and the apathy, and this hospital was no exception. Patients on good wards sit around the walls, some in chairs, some on the floor. Attendants on wards with good morale are likely to be found shooting pool with a favorite patient or chatting together; on wards with bad morale attendants may be sitting reading comic books. Either way, patients go untreated.

We have described in detail in other works [2,3,4] how the problem of improving this hospital was attacked, and we shall use similar illustrations on the following pages. With the close cooperation of the Clinical Director, I. L. W. Clancey, and with the backing of the Medical Superintendent, Dr. Humphry Osmond, it was possible to build a therapeutic milieu—mainly in group settings—through the creation of new roles, the reallocation of responsibility and authority, and such cultural changes as the re-education of ward attendants. This enabled us to reactivate the patients, in stable groups wherever possible. Perhaps the most effective innovation was the mobilization of the therapeutic potential of the senior, norm-bearing ward staff.

Three years after its reorganization, the hospital was given the American Psychiatric Association's Achievement Award in acknowledgment of improvements in these areas as well as in others in which we were less directly involved.

The Kansas City Receiving Center is a small, acute treatment hospital housed in a new and pleasant building. It is part of the City Hospital system of Kansas City, Missouri, but although it cares for the indigent mentally ill of the city and receives its major financial support from the city, it is administered by a private, nonprofit foundation: the Greater Kansas City Mental Health Foundation. This arrangement provides a useful flexibility of operation. Further, the support of the Foundation made it financially possible to embark on some experimental programs.

Dr. Milton Kirkpatrick was the Director of the hospital for the major part of our stay. We joined a group who already had a considerable commitment to the ideas of milieu therapy: Dr. Robert H. Barnes, now the hospital's Director; Dr. Robijn Hornstra, now its Clinical Director; Dr. Lee Hanes, now the Director of a new Day Hospital; and Mrs. Ruth Lewis, Director of Nurses. Our early preoccupations were with increasing patient freedom, creating a more therapeutic role for our nurses, and developing methods of restoring the orientation of newly admitted patients and decreasing their anxiety. We attempted to link these procedures to the individual psychotherapy and drug treatments already in use. Evaluation of results indicated, however, that individual psychotherapy served to lengthen hospital stay without apparently influencing the probability of relapse. Further, when the average period of hospitalization was less than thirty days, it seemed unlikely that psychotherapy could accomplish much in such a short time or that any damage would be done by delaying it until the patient could return home. Because of this, in-patient psychotherapy was discontinued and offered to suitable patients only on an out-patient basis after discharge. Lately, an active follow-up clinic and day hospital have been added to conventional services. The hospital was awarded the American Psychiatric Association's Achievement Award in 1961.

References

[1] PAUL SIVADON, LLEWELLYN DAVIES, and A. BAKER, *A Ground Plan for Psychiatry* (WHO Bulletin, 1959).

[2] ELAINE CUMMING and JOHN CUMMING, "The Locus of Power in a Large Mental Hospital," *Psychiatry*, XIX, 4 (1956), 361.

[3] ELAINE CUMMING, I. L. W. CLANCEY, and JOHN CUMMING, "Improving Patient Care Through Organizational Changes in the Mental Hospital," *Psychiatry*, XIX, 3 (1956), 249.

[4] JOHN CUMMING and ELAINE CUMMING, "Social Equilibrium and Social Change in the Large Mental Hospital," in M. Greenblatt, D. J. Levinson, and R. H. Williams (eds.), *The Patient and the Mental Hospital* (Glencoe, Ill.: Free Press, 1957).

CHAPTER 5

The Physical Setting

We take our everyday physical milieu for granted most of the time; nevertheless, as Anthony Wallace has pointed out (in "Mazeway Disintegration"), we cherish its familiarity. Furthermore, we orient ourselves by its cues and use it for reinforcing identity.

The effect of physical space can be seen in everyday situations. For example, the old-fashioned doctor's office, although often crowded and uncomfortable, was unassuming and quite personal. The waiting room of a modern middle-class practitioner is impersonal and minimizes interaction. The patients may be guided to individual examining rooms as fast as they appear. The receptionist is a traffic director; her relationship with the patients is formal.

In the crowded waiting rooms of free clinics patients are closer to one another than to the doctor—it is not surprising that group therapy started among patients waiting in a tuberculosis follow-up clinic. The busy physician moved his chair into the waiting room and joined the conversation.[1]

The physical environment in which patients are treated

can be discussed in terms of the information it gives about the
goals and values of the society that provides it, and its contribution to the patient's identity, orientation, and ego organization, at a time when his openness provides an opportunity
for ego growth. The physical setting can also be regarded in
terms of the assistance it gives to the people who care for the
patient and in terms of the ego problems that it provides for
solution.

PHYSICAL SETTING AND SOCIAL GOALS
AND VALUES

Hospital buildings reveal something of how society views
the activities that go on within them. The grim facades of our
isolated state hospitals told us what their designers thought
about the mentally ill. Later, the redesigned interiors reflected
a new goal of restoring the psychotic to normal functioning
in society.*

All hospitals have hierarchies of goals and the architecture
often reveals them. If a nurse must spend all her time locking
and unlocking doors and escorting patients to distant places,
custody ranks higher than treatment. In traditional state hospitals the farm buildings usually were in better condition than
the hospitals themselves. Only when the farms stopped making
money did most hospitals relinquish them as primary goals, to
which caring for patients was secondary.

A more benign form of custody, based upon the assumption that the patients were incurable, was indicated by the
"self-sufficiency of the plant." Hospitals with self-sufficiency
as a primary goal prided themselves on providing their own

---

* The important fields of hospital design, color therapy, and so on are
beyond the range of this book. We are concerned only with environmental
minima in our discussion of the physical setting; although it is likely that
much can be contributed to the care of the mentally ill through good
design.

churches, bowling alleys, stores, and recreation centers so that patients did not have to leave the hospital grounds. Many patients are still cut off from society by being in hospitals which themselves furnish all the necessary services. It undoubtedly is preferable, however, for hospitals to own their own fleet of buses and thus demonstrate their attachment to the greater society by transporting patients to outside facilities when the occasion indicates their use.

In general, although locks and window grills and "indestructible" furniture were the outward and visible signs of a set of beliefs about the mentally ill, it cannot be assumed that their absence automatically means good care. For example, in a hospital without bars on the windows, if at mealtime an attendant comes to the door of a chronic male ward and shouts, "Dinner!" and sixty men get up and shuffle silently to the dining room, there might as well be bars on the windows.

The hospital layout has characteristically disregarded the convenience of the attendants and nurses; the facilities provided have been of the worst kind, suggesting that the low evaluation of the patients has carried over onto the attendants who care for them.

We have described elsewhere (in "The Locus of Power in a Large Mental Hospital") how Weyburn Hospital, when we first saw it, had virtually no tools—for cooking, for cleaning, for repairs—that were not obsolete.* Furthermore, the living and recreation arrangements provided for the staff were equally substandard.

The pariah role of patients and staff alike was equally clear in another large hospital where, at the time, the vegetables

---

* These deprivations were by then under vigorous attack by D. G. McKerracher, the Director of the Psychiatric Services branch of the Department of Health of the Government of Saskatchewan, but he had many years of neglect and hopelessness to overcome. Furthermore, constructive requests from *within* the hospital had, at that time, yet to show their effectiveness in winning legislative support.

were prepared in a dark underground room in which patients sat all day, on a concrete floor and amidst wet detritus, around a pit filled with filthy water into which they dipped the vegetables they were peeling. The staff idled at their backs, "guarding" them. A doctor, accustomed to watching this scene and sharing society's evaluation of his patients, explained to one of us that for melancholic patients this work was therapeutic.

It is not necessary to give more examples; Albert Deutsch [2] has adequately documented this type of squalor. From such environments patients must accept reflections of their identity. Ironically, in a revulsion from this kind of treatment, some hospital directors have provided their patients with a hotel-like sumptuousness. Although this does not offer the patients degraded concepts of themselves, it is, for most of them, hopelessly ego-alien.*

In terms of our theory, inappropriate surroundings mean that any kind of tolerable ego feeling is obtained either by a degradation of ego organization to the low level that we recognize as "chronicity" or by a shift toward a kind of environment essentially unrelated to post-discharge reality. What, then, should be the specifications of an ideal therapeutic physical milieu?

GENERAL ORIENTATION AND THE PHYSICAL SETTING

Orientation is not perfected until maturity. When an absent-minded twelve-year-old says, "Was that my lunch or dinner I just ate?" he reveals that he cannot yet automatically locate himself in time by physical cues. Orientation in space and time are such important ego functions that, in the extreme

---

* For a discussion of this point, see the work of Polansky, White, and Miller.[3]

case, many normal people become disturbed and even hallucinated when all physical cues are removed. When physical cues are present but ambiguous they lead to disrupted ego feeling, disorientation, and anxiety. The reason for this is simple. As Parsons has pointed out in *The Social System,* the expectations of one person act as a sanction on another and, as a rule, move him to conform to these expectations. The messages of the environment are clear sanctions on the patient to act appropriately to it: to be violent, or slovenly, or antisocial. If he does act in these ways, and if the ward staff has learned to think of such behavior as the usual manifestation of mental illness, the patient will find that the staff will confirm his behavior, a new ego organization will have begun, orientation will have been established, and he will be a step nearer the chronic wards.

For a number of reasons, orientation has been used extensively to gauge the patient's psychiatric condition. Traditionally, it has been divided into orientation in time, to place, and to person. Orientation to person is determined by whether or not the patient knows his name and legal identity, but it does not usually include any of the complex and variable ideas that people have about themselves. There is evidence that any change requiring ego reorganization will bring about some set dedifferentiation and diffusion feeling, resulting in a change in self concept or orientation to self. It is a common phenomenon, for example, to hear people express new ideas about themselves after their first serious physical illness in adult life. The concept of self will vary as life patterns change, and, within such long-range changes, it will vary from clear to ambiguous as ego diffusion is experienced. Thus, the failure of orientation to the self seen in some psychotic patients is merely the end point of a state of constantly fluctuating self-perception. The environment must provide cues that firmly establish at least a public identity if other sources of ego diffusion are to be overcome. This can be partly accomplished by providing specific opportunities for maintaining orientation, some of which are outlined below.

Orientation in time is usually judged, in the clinical situation, by the patient's knowledge of the current date. However, this crude measure misses the range of subtleties involved in remaining oriented to time. It may not even have the virtue of being an end point because the lack of cues in the environment regarding time often accounts for failure.

Both Federn and Erikson emphasize the importance of a sense of continuity for maintaining identity feeling. When identity is lost in sleep, we must feel that it will be taken up again with an accompanying sense of continuity upon awakening. Ego identity itself incorporates the idea of continuity and expectation of sameness, or predictable change, as part of its definition. The individual stands at a nodal point between his past and a future that he expects to be recognizably similar to the present or, more precisely, reconcilable with his projected identity—it should never be forgotten that any therapeutic milieu is a *temporary* arrangement, and the patient must always be helped to project a post-clinic or post-hospital self concept and ego identity.

The organization of all experience is like verbal communication: it gains its meaning by the arrangement the symbols are given in time; to deliver the words of a sentence in random temporal order is to destroy the meaning. The ability to organize sequences of past experience and to project them into the future may well be one of the more important ego organizations.

THE PHYSICAL SETTING AND SPECIFIC
AIDS TO ORIENTATION

Many specific physical features of the environment can assist the patient in remaining oriented. In the first place, the physical milieu should be related to the backgrounds of those to be treated there in order to maintain continuity, familiarity, and, thereby, identity feeling. Even people of robust ego are troubled by unfamiliar surroundings: classically, the ocean voyage gives rise to feelings of unreality and diffusion. In particular, furnishings for offices, clinics, day centers, and hospitals should be similar to those in general use elsewhere and of good quality; they should be neither cheap and shoddy nor overelaborate but should assist orientation to place by containing elements of familiarity. Paul Sivadon and his fellow authors (in *A Ground Plan for Psychiatry*) point out that materials such as leather are universally recognized as being of good quality and yet are not pretentious. Smaller items should reflect the general desire of patients. Professional staff often choose "arty" things that patients consider peculiar.* Furthermore, to anticipate Part III, the choice of smaller furnishings is an excellent subject for problem solution. Similarly, pet animals and birds both render the milieu familiar and create resolvable problems.

As well as general cultural familiarity, the milieu must provide practical and concrete markings for the disoriented. In the large mental hospital, for example, unmarked doors are almost always a problem for patients, especially new patients. Locked doors should be given such marks as "Storeroom—staff only" to reduce the uncertainty that they represent, and all other doors should be equally well labeled. Some hospitals use color to indicate types of areas. Patients should be taught the geography of the ward. One of the more poignant parts of *The Snake Pit* [5] is a description of disorientation: the author

---

* It is probably true that wherever it is possible to introduce attractive things with good design *that the patients like*, this should be done, but Davis [4] has shown that many things which intellectuals find attractive seem austere and "unhomelike" to working-class people. The goal is not to improve the patient's taste but to cure his illness.

was moved from one ward to another when she became disturbed, but she experienced the move, in her confusion, as a mysterious geographic shift in which the dayroom was where the dormitory had been and the dormitory took the place of the dayroom. Confusion of this kind can almost always be avoided.

Each person who deals with patients is part of the structure of the situation and must be clearly identified both as to who he is and as to his role with regard to the patient. Many clinic patients who are by no means very ill are disturbed by the anonymity of the person to whom they tell their intimate affairs. In out-patient clinics the staff members may find it amusing that social workers are taken for doctors because of their white coats. In hospitals mistakes such as this are more serious, because ambiguities leading to confusion and embarrassment can result from lack of labels, and the patient has no outside anchor points by which to reorient himself. Although some ambiguities should be faced by all but the sickest patients, it should be by design, not chance. In some hospitals nurses have their names on their uniforms, and, in others, staff members with differing duties wear colors designating their various functions. In the Kansas City Receiving Center, photographs of people who often visited the ward were posted on a bulletin board. In larger hospitals a floor plan can help.

Arrangements for visitors should be flexible. Patients may want visitors to participate in ward activities, and this should sometimes be made possible, although decisions on such participation should be made between the patients and the nurses. Other patients may need access to visiting rooms so that they can see their visitors privately.*

---

* In passing, density of population seems to be important for ego development but it is not clear why. Plant,[6] in a sensitive analysis of the effects of overcrowding on children, points out that people are uncomfortable in situations where the numbers are either greater or fewer than

To assist the patient in his orientation, the physical milieu should give him ample access to his own appearance. All patients should have mirrors freely available to them, and at least one of the mirrors should be full length in order to help the patient reaffirm his body image and keep up to date on his appearance.[7] Arrangements for grooming and for bathing should resemble those that people customarily use under normal circumstances—that is, they should be private and no more scheduled than absolutely necessary. A normal array of soap, toothpaste, hair tonic, cosmetics, and the like should also be freely available. The patient should wear his own clothing wherever possible; but if this is not possible, clothing should be obtained in a place that resembles a shop, the patient should have as much choice as possible, and he should be provided with a place to keep his clothing neat. Laundry, dry cleaning, and repairs should be available, preferably in the greater community.

In many hospitals, hard-pressed superintendents argue that such personalized arrangements are too expensive, no matter how desirable. For example, at one time in Weyburn Hospital the men all wore expensive work boots or went unshod. For some old men the boots were too heavy; they went unshod, which limited their activities and kept them apathetic and withdrawn. Furthermore, when repaired boots were returned to the ward, they were reissued without the consideration of who the original owners were. Some men would not wear the repaired boots because they did not fit and instead continued to wear their own boots until they were past repair. A central shoe shop with a variety of styles of shoes and boots and with repair facilities was planned in collaboration

---

they are accustomed to. For this reason, if there are people from both country and city in a hospital, it is hard to arrange matters to suit them all. It is clear, however, that overcrowding in hospitals is directly related to acts of violence; but whether or not it *causes* violence is uncertain.

with the ward staff, but eventually other matters became more pressing and, like many other good plans, it never came to fruition. However, a plan to supply lightweight shoes to those not needing work boots and to allow patients to have their own shoes repaired did reduce costs considerably. At the same time, the patients were benefited by having their own shoes, and chronic patients, especially, profited from learning how to get their shoes repaired.

A patient must be given every opportunity to remain oriented to the place in which he is being treated and to his own person, but, perhaps most basically, he must be kept oriented in time.

All therapeutic milieus should have calendars and clocks in salient positions. All should have a wide variety of daily and weekly papers, preferably "home town" papers. All menus, programs, and memorandums should be dated, and social events should be scheduled and identified by date and time. These dating features are especially important if patients have had electric shock. Disorientation after shock is often taken for granted, but it can be relieved by simple techniques that immeasurably assist in avoiding much confusion. We have seen a man with Korsakoff's syndrome retrained, by a ward aide in daily sessions, to tell the time and date. Resolution of the time problem was the first step in ordering this patient's perceptions more rationally.

In general, it is necessary to have a firm sense of the flow of time and a firm grasp of its meaning in order to anticipate the future. This means that the self can be projected forward and ego organizations differentiated in terms of the future. This is one of the more important ways in which the effects of failure can be delimited and ego organization maintained.

PHYSICAL MILIEU AS AN AID TO SOCIAL STRUCTURE

In Chapter 4 we said that among the more important things the milieu must provide are a series of graded and controlled crises for a patient to resolve and a staff of helpful people to assist him in the process. The physical surroundings can either help or hinder the staff member in carrying out his facilitating role.

In general, physical arrangements make an impact upon the course of social events. When a staff meets, for example, the position of the various kinds of staff members can be used to predict their behavior. If a doctor sits at the head of a table with residents beside him, medical students around the table, and nurses away from the table in two neat rows, the nurses will behave like an audience. For teaching, this is useful; if the nurses have information the doctors want, however, it is not a good physical arrangement for eliciting it.

In a hospital the physical location of services, together with locked doors, can effectively keep a nurse from doing anything except run errands. This situation also can keep a patient from taking part in any structured activity. But the environment can favor nursing ease and patient interaction if nurses, aides, and patients cooperate in arranging it. For example, a mobile cart to deliver supplies, records, and messages to all wards several times a day can spare nursing time. A "treaty" with the maintenance department can serve the double purpose of getting repairs done and involving the maintenance people in the problem-solving milieu. Not all added facilities, however, prove to be therapeutic. One mixed ward of men and women had worked out a routine for housekeeping. When a new floor-cleaning machine was introduced, it removed a simple group activity before the staff was prepared to develop another to take its place. More familiar types of regular household equipment would probably have been better to have and would have provided problems concerning the rights and obligations in sex-linked roles. All changes have therapeutic potential if properly planned; it is for this planning that the doctor's theoretical knowledge is needed.

From the nurses' point of view, the ward should be easy to clean and should have storage space. The nurse should be assisted by the arrangement of the ward in meeting the needs of the patients. For example, if the dayroom is at a distance from the nursing station, the nurse can check the ward as she goes back and forth and thus find patients who have retired to their rooms weeping or depressed. In general, patients tend to congregate near the nursing station, and this is the most important consideration in planning it.

Nurses and aides can usually suggest ways to save time. On one occasion, in Weyburn Hospital, aides suggested cutting a door between two large adjacent rooms in a geriatrics ward, which resulted in a 20 per cent saving of time. Only these aides could have realized how much time was being wasted because there was no easy passage between the rooms.

The size of wards is important. The World Health Organization suggests that no more than thirty-two patients should be on one ward, and then it should be subdivided into groups of eight patients each. Eight appears to be the largest group in which it is possible for one person to be sensitive to each member's interactions and to fully observe the tone and temper of the remainder of the group. When there are more than eight people, some are likely to go "out of field." However, groups can also be too small. If there are only three or four people, there is a danger of intense affects developing among them, along with unnecessary vulnerability to loss and overuse of one set of relationships at the expense of others requiring different ego organizations.

If the ward contains more than thirty-two people, it is possible for some to be isolated.* Also, there is greater likelihood of a kind of shifting and regrouping because of cross-cutting routines that break down group structure. For example, a group from a large ward may plan something and be disrupted by the order that some of them are scheduled to go to the dentist. Although membership in a cohesive group is not an end in itself, our theory suggests that membership in a small, stable, informal group should precede multiple memberships and that these informal groups should contain patients at varying stages of recovery, as well as nurses.

In many old hospitals, minor alterations and rearrangements can make it easier for small patient groups to live together. For example, furniture can be regrouped to create functional areas that give a kind of privacy. In many mental hospitals, furniture is arranged in such a way that no interaction is possible. Chairs in straight rows used to be a frequent sight even before television—itself an interesting problem creator—made it less unreasonable. In Weyburn Hospital's chronic wards, the huge dayrooms were lined around the edges with chairs—like an enormous waiting room. The patients, however, usually sat on the floor in the hallways watching the attendants, and occasionally a doctor, pass by. This may have been the selector temperament in operation maintaining ego equilibrium. In principle, it is better to equip with living arrangements the places where interaction is highest—for patients will seek these out.

Any mental hospital or day center should provide physical

---

* It is ironical that the old "Kirkbride" building, now considered outdated, has, from this point of view, an ideal layout. Dr. Herman Snow of Ogdensburg, New York, the superintendent of an excellent state hospital which still has these old buildings, tells us that they are his best physical settings. The Kirkbride is basically a rectangle divided lengthwise. One half is a dayroom and corridor combined and the other is a row of patients' rooms. In such an arrangement a patient can be alone, be in his room with the door open, or out in the group, but wherever he is, the nursing staff can know and take account of it.

facilities for work or worklike activity. The subject of work is always so important that it will later be dealt with at length. In general, it is of paramount importance that the environment allows for a wide range of both instrumental and socioemotional roles. Ideally, a hospital should have an auditorium large enough to seat all the patients and at least half the staff so that formal business can be done in the way that it is sometimes done outside. There should be rooms of a variety of sizes for ward meetings and club gatherings and small spaces suitable for group therapy. There should be provision for privacy. In short, there should be facilities for a range of activities which simulate the worlds of work, family, recreation, and voluntary association.

Such a variety of activities will provide needed practice in developing ego organizations, in using them appropriately, and in keeping them differentiated. Although patients may enter only the familiar activities at first, most, eventually, can be encouraged to participate in a reasonably wide variety of activities.

PHYSICAL SETTING AND PROBLEM SOLVING

Problem solution or crisis resolution lies at the heart of our theory. The main purpose of the physical milieu is to provide a setting in which the patient is supported by a feeling of familiarity and continuity and in which the staff is free to help him toward ego growth. Nevertheless, the physical environment is not just a background, and in itself it offers many natural problems for solution. As we have said previously, the choice of a piece of furniture or equipment is an excellent problem, especially for women, because it requires attention to a decision that for most people is similar to those they must make every day. Furthermore, it requires sufficient interpersonal skill for reaching agreement with others in the making of the decision, but the decision is one that need have no very severe or far-reaching consequences. In an English hospital, we saw patients and staff together, dressed in overalls, busily chipping down a brick partition. The men had been remodeling their ward for a long time and had been making a constant series of decisions about how to proceed and how to live with the mess in the meantime.

The physical milieu is perhaps best if there is always something left to do or to change. This is especially so if it involves the patients' ways of life. Furthermore, there is, in all milieu programs, a sense of ragged edges and unfinished business that may be painful for the staff to endure and disappointing to visitors but is nevertheless quite vital to the success of the program. For example, in a small psychiatric teaching hospital, a male and a female ward were integrated into one mixed ward after much planning and discussion. Two days later a resident reported in a staff meeting that eating and recreational activities had been integrated successfully but that no attempt had been made to integrate the sleeping arrangements until two women got into a fight and one of them asked to be put in a room at the other end of the ward. This was thought to be a reasonable request, and discussion elicited the suggestion that one of the men should exchange rooms with her; this shift was agreed upon by all. Thus, the problem of whether or not men should sleep on the "female" ward was solved as a by-product of separating the two women. Later, in the same discussion, it transpired that a male patient had told a medical student that he was glad that the wards had been integrated because it "makes it more like it is outside." Another patient said that he liked it because with the door between the wards open there wasn't "all that slamming all day long." *

---

* It is easy to overlook the fact that the normal sounds associated with work can be maddening to people trying to read or to rest and are particularly disruptive to patients whose anxiety is high.

However, one woman expressed considerable fear about being among men. A nurse then reported that some patients were anxious because one of the women had undressed in front of the men, and they feared it might happen again. The staff planned to discuss—first with the women and eventually with the whole patient group—standards of modesty in a mixed ward, in the hope of developing ground rules for the ward. In this kind of executive function activity, problems of impulse control can be recognized and dealt with.

These excerpts from a staff discussion not only illustrate the range of problems that a shift in living arrangements can offer but give some idea of the fluidity of the situation and of the numbers and kinds of problems that must be faced all at once in a ward attempting a change. The problems that the physical environment offers point up the paradox discussed in Chapter 4; an important function of the physical milieu is to lower ambiguity—but problems are in their nature ambiguous. Although resolution of the ambiguity in the planned problem contributes to ego growth, gratuitous sources of ambiguity can raise anxiety and freeze the will. The physical environment is less important in clinics than in hospitals because the patient is not so dependent on it for clarification. It can be very important in the home, and we shall comment on it briefly in Chapter 12.

In summary, the ego-damaged patient suffering from loss of ego sets through disuse or biological accident may need specific retraining, and the physical environment can assist in the process. If he is suffering from ego dedifferentiation and spreading then diffusion feelings, fear, and anxiety can be ameliorated by an environment that is culturally familiar, that does not devalue the patient by its poverty, and that gives him clear, unambiguous, and consistent clues as to time, place, and person. Finally, ego ability can be enhanced by the physical environment if it is neither too sheltering nor too difficult and if it can provide a range of problems for solution that have some relationship to his life outside the hospital.

In discussing the physical setting we have touched upon the people in it as part of the "structure of the situation." In the next chapter we shall discuss in some detail those aspects of the social structure particularly related to the allocation of authority.

References

[1] HENRY JOSEPH PRATT, "The Class Method in Home Treatment of Tuberculosis and What it has Accomplished," *Boston Medical and Surgical Journal*, CLXVI, 8 (1912), 280.

[2] ALBERT DEUTSCH, *The Shame of the States* (New York: Harcourt, Brace, 1948).

[3] NORMAN A. POLANSKY, ROBERT B. WHITE, and STUART C. MILLER, "Determinants of the Role-Image of the Patient in a Psychiatric Hospital," in M. Greenblatt, D. J. Levinson, and R. H. Williams (eds.), *The Patient and the Mental Hospital* (Glencoe, Ill.: Free Press, 1957).

[4] JAMES DAVIS, "Cultural Factors in the Perception of Status Symbols," *Midwest Sociologist*, XXI, 1 (1958), 1.

[5] MARY JANE WARD, *The Snake Pit* (New York: Random House, 1946).

[6] JAMES S. PLANT, *Personality and the Cultural Pattern* (New York: The Commonwealth Fund, 1937).

[7] FRANKLYN N. ARNHOFF, "Self-Body Recognition in Schizophrenia" (paper read to the Annual Meetings of the American Psychological Association, New York City, 1961).

CHAPTER 6

Authority and Control

We have described some ways in which the physical environment can contribute to the therapeutic milieu; now we shall discuss the problem of authority and how its allocation can influence the process of ego restitution.

Like the physical structure of the hospital, the authority structure reveals society's evaluation of the mentally ill. At the time that the bars were put on hospital windows * an authoritarian society existed within these hospitals. Sometimes it was benevolently despotic, but often it was cruelly repressive, and either way reflected belief in the incurability and helplessness of the patient. The reconstruction of the buildings and the removal of some of their worst features usually have been accompanied by a redistribution of authority commensurate with newer ideas of treatment. However, it is easier to renovate the buildings than to remotivate the patients, and unfortunately a vigorous building program does not guarantee better treatment.

---

* It should be remembered that many of the worst hospitals were conceived in the best tradition of moral treatment and later degraded to their present level.

Most of the mentally ill are treated in situations overtly created by society for the control of deviance,* and society is the final source of authority for what goes on in its hospitals. As members of society, however, we have two conflicting motives for treating patients: we wish to be humane to the mentally ill, but we also wish to protect ourselves from those who have slipped out of the web of predictable social behavior. A conflict is also built into the *treatment* of the ill: it is authorized by society, but it must be done on behalf of both society and the patient who has, in a sense, failed that society. Treatment must include both support and control, and therefore it is hard for it to escape having a flavor of punishment as well as of healing.

THREE SOURCES OF AUTHORITY

Authority is paradoxical in nature since a person in authority is able to make people do only what they are already willing to do. If people are not willing, *power* is needed, but even then power cannot always prevail.[2] Thus, when an officer tells his troops to march, they march because they already intended to. However, it is *not* this central characteristic of authority that concerns us here but, rather, a secondary aspect —the right to make the decision to give the order in the first place. From our point of view, the critical aspect of authority is the location of this right. First, however, we shall discuss briefly the three major sources of authority: the traditional, the charismatic, and the rational-legal.[3]

Traditional authority is familiar to us in the family—the father is usually the final authority. There is traditional author- ity in hospitals also—as when people have certain rights just

---

* The public mental hospitals supply 849,644 of the nation's mental hospital beds. The Veterans' hospitals supply another 119,403, and Fed- eral hospitals another 6,549. General hospital beds and research and teaching hospital beds amount to another 124,474, and many of these are publicly supported. There are 80,807 private beds.[1]

because of their long tenure, or when it is expected that some role holders will exercise authority even when "everyone knows" allocating authority by these criteria is inefficient.

Occasionally an individual is able to make other people believe he has authority just because he says he has. This is *charismatic* authority and it is solely a quality of the relationship between the leader and the led. Some doctors are able to establish this kind of authority, but it is unstable because it demands intense personal loyalty and commitment and because it generates factions and is therefore unsuitable to large, complex organizations. Furthermore, charismatic authority cannot be passed on; when a charismatic leader leaves, his authority either dies or becomes routinized as the third type—rational-legal authority.

Rational-legal authority has its source in role specifications. It is a rational authority legitimized by the rules governing admission to roles. In the hospital, for example, the role of Superintendent of Nurses carries with it authority over all the other nurses. It is *not* the nurse herself who has the authority, it is the office. When she leaves, the authority is transferred from her to a similarly qualified role holder.

Rational-legal authority is associated with what we call bureaucracy—indeed, any large hierarchized rational-legal structure is a bureaucracy. It is well to remember that there is nothing evil in bureaucracy as such; it is simply one way of organizing the work of the world. If the goal of a bureaucracy is the restitution of damaged egos and its organization is efficient, there is no reason to believe that it cannot succeed, even though it may face unique problems in doing so.

In all rational-legal structures, however, there are islands of traditional authority. In some cases they add flavor and a sense of continuity, but more often they lead to pathological obstructions of purpose. By the same token, charismatic authority may sometimes appear with a new staff member who launches a crusade for improvement. Sometimes this results in permanent gain but often in disappointment and cynicism because the changes do not last. When such people leave, their authority usually reverts to those who had it before.

We shall now turn to the problem of decision making, one of the most important aspects of the allocation of authority.

LOCATION OF DECISIONS

In any social structure, decisions should be made at the places in which they can most effectively forward the goals of the structure, once the major values *about* decision making itself have been taken into account. A certain amount of decentralization of decision making is considered morally desirable in American society, no matter what its effect; "authoritarianism" is believed to be too big a price to pay for efficiency.

In general, decision making should be located according to whether policy or action is involved and according to the generality or specificity of the decisions to be made. For example, the Clinical Director of a hospital can decide that patients shall wear their own, rather than hospital, clothes, but the patient, perhaps helped by a nurse, must decide himself which of his clothes to wear each day. Those at the apex of the structure cannot be sufficiently acquainted with day-to-day operations to make concrete operating decisions.

This principle is generally true of both the mental hospital and the clinic, but before we go into detail it is important to deal with a pervasive misunderstanding about the location of decision making.

Democratic social structure is generally conceded to be valuable, but those who value it often confuse it with egalitarian social structure. Briefly, democracy in a bureaucratic organization refers to a decision-making process, and it consists in the staff members having something to say about the course of their

working day. It does *not* consist in everyone having something
to say about everything. In some factories, for example, a
supervisor may have a large number of people under his
control who have nothing at all to say about their conditions
of work. At the same time, they may all be subject to the same
rules and the same working conditions regardless of differences
in skills and wages. Such a system is undemocratic, but, as it
has only one echelon of people with equal rights and privileges,
it is relatively egalitarian. In contrast, most hospitals have a
hierarchy because people are ranked in terms of education,
training, and salary. Nonetheless, such hospitals can be democratic if the staff is encouraged to contribute ideas about how
the wards should be run and these ideas are heeded. This,
although democratic, is an inegalitarian operation. During the
last decade, progressive hospital directors have moved, in the
name of democracy, toward a wider dispersal of the right to
make decisions. This has made the therapeutic milieu possible
because the essence of the problem-solving process is the right
to make decisions at the time and place most likely to lead to
ego restitution. This increase in the kinds of staff members
with the *right* to make decisions has brought with it an emphasis upon free and open communication that, in turn, has
often led to the working out of differences of opinion among
several staff echelons. However, there have been problems and
strains associated with this redistribution of authority and
especially with the efflorescence of communication for its own
sake. Amitai Etzioni [4] has pointed out the fallacy of imagining
that all administrative troubles can be cured through what he
calls the "human relations approach," and he has suggested that
overcommunication can be time-consuming and distracting.
Where, then, in the therapeutic milieu should the decision-
making process be located, and where should the information
be pooled? In general, authority should lie where it best
serves the goals of the system—that is, with the personnel charged

with the therapeutic task. Information, however, should be distributed through the staff echelons in terms of the types of decisions being made. Ward staff should have easy access to all the information relevant to the problem-solving process on the ward.

Patients in hospitals and day centers spend almost all their time in the company of the staff members lowest in the hierarchy, and it is these staff members who must create a problem-solving climate. It is for this reason, and not because of its intrinsic worth, that extreme decentralization is so important. Many important, concrete decisions about patients must be located at the level of the nurses, the attendants, the patients themselves, and even the cleaners and maintenance men.* Furthermore, the need to make decisions at this level is so imperative to the existence of the society that decisions *are* made whether or not the authority is delegated. Failure to delegate results in decisions being hidden, and usually these are antitherapeutic. For example, in the Kansas City Receiving Center the male ward attendants did not know whether or not they had the authority to allow sleepless patients to get out of bed to smoke cigarettes or walk around the corridors. Because the attendants were in doubt, they made the decision with the fewest consequences and insisted that the patients remain in bed. When they later had the authority to use their own discretion, they then allowed the patients to get up and talk with them, to smoke, to read, or to engage in any activity they felt would help the patients to fall asleep.

It is fortunate that general democratic values coincide with expediency in the running of hospitals, but it should be re-

---

* Since this was written, there has come to our attention a movement in large hospitals toward decentralization. That is, a large hospital divides itself up into smaller, semiautonomous units.[5] As the maintenance is still central, this has the fortunate secondary effect of pointing up the fact that care of patients requires a different type of social structure and administration from laundering sheets.

membered that decentralization is not an *easy* solution to the problems of the treatment institution. It requires careful planning to insure that information flows up and down and across the structure and arrives where it is needed, and it requires more planning, coordination, and vigilance than a central organization requires.

Granted that the authority to make important decisions should be vested in patients and ward staffs, how can this be accomplished? Beginning at the top, the agents of society, whether they are boards of directors or government departments, must give the directors of hospitals and clinics a clear mandate to act in the patients' best interests within the limits of the laws surrounding the directors' operations.

The limits of the law often define the ways in which a patient must enter the hospital, and they affect his civil liberties in ways that range from his freedom to have a driver's license to his right to vote. In Great Britain, changes in the laws encouraged informal admission to mental hospitals, revolutionized the practice of psychiatry, and profoundly changed the role of the medical director.

The director of any hospital must mediate between the agents of the society and the institution and balance the needs of both. Therefore, as the director must serve two masters, he in turn must delegate the major part of his therapeutic authority * to others who can, in a protected situation, take the part of the patients. It is inherent in all therapeutic relationships that the therapist is an agent of society on the one hand and a friend of the patient on the other. If he were not, he would not be able to represent "wellness" in his interactions with his patients. This is particularly important for ward staff who may at times react automatically to the patients' non-normativeness

---

* Only a medical doctor is legally allowed, because of his training, to make the decisions about life and death that occasionally must be made.

in terms of general values and beliefs. These reactions should always be recognized as legitimate even if they are not in every case encouraged. These automatic reactions of staff to such things as sexual acting-out are the price that must be paid for having a society on the wards that is rooted in a nondeviant culture. It is the task of the director to give his professional staff the right to distribute their authority to nurses and aides and patients wherever it is therapeutic to do so. He must defend this practice when it comes under attack, whether it comes from those—usually doctors and psychologists—who consider the ward staff "too judgmental" or from the lay public who consider that both staff and patients have "too much freedom." In general, those in top positions must balance the interests of society against the interests of the patients when making general policy, while those in constant contact with the patients should have the authority to make specific, concrete decisions—in terms of the patients' illnesses—as to whether any particular deviant act should be tolerated or sanctioned.

Medically trained people must work patiently toward delegating to nurses and aides a much wider spectrum of authority to make decisions than they are accustomed to accepting—or than doctors are accustomed to granting. In a therapeutic milieu this means, paradoxically, that doctors must take responsibility for details that do not seem on the face of it to be medically relevant. Thus, a doctor may take many hours to arrange for materials to be available to a group of patients so that they can build a picnic shelter or a bandstand or an outdoor oven. In short, whereas doctors must, in the therapeutic milieu, give up the authority that they have been used to exercising so that nurses and aides may make decisions without delay, they must at the same time exercise administrative authority of a kind not traditionally medical. For many doctors this is hard, but the creation of the therapeutic environment hinges on their being able to do it.

By the same token, nurses and aides must learn to assume authority that they have not had before. This is more difficult still, for it involves fear of failure and of reprisals. It is best done through group interaction, which supports the individual and develops the norms, values, and sentiments that give identity to the working group.[6]

Communication between doctors and ward staff must be unimpeded. Clear lines of communication are essential to the functioning of a bureaucracy, and those who make policy decisions must act as communication centers so that decisions can be based on accurate assessments of reality. But in a hospital, there must also be confidence among the ward staff that they can quickly get correct information and, what is more important, support and backing when they need it. As a matter of fact, in most hospitals communication flows downward informally, and, because they are in contact with so many kinds of staff people, patients are usually the first to know the latest rumors. The therapeutic milieu has to be built to send authority and accurate information downward and correct information upward.

A doctor who sets out to create a therapeutic environment —given that he has the necessary backing from his administration—might well start with a ward meeting. It is probably best that he be named ward administrator and made responsible for the operation of the ward. At first, the doctor and his ward staff can meet alone and discuss problems involved in providing a situation in which patients can make decisions. Initially, problems will have a minimum of detail and will probably concern discipline: "Joe Smith hit George Green in the face —what should we do?" The doctor at this point must resist the temptation to deliver a lecture on aggressivity. His task is to demonstrate that there is a way of dealing with these problems and that the staff can find it. He should probably turn to the lowest-ranking person in the group, address that person by name, and ask him a question. This person is chosen because in the ordinary course of events he is unlikely to offer information. Furthermore, once someone with higher status has spoken, the lower-ranking member will usually be unwilling to offer any information that might appear contradictory. It is important that the senior members of the ward staff be prepared for this method of running a group meeting, otherwise they may—in nonverbal ways—discourage their juniors from participating. In this instance, the doctor may ask: "You happened to be near when this happened; what do you usually do in these cases?" Or, "Has Mr. Smith * been upset lately? What do you think should be done?" If he does not deliberately bring in everyone who may have something to contribute, the meeting will tend to become a panel between the doctor and the one or two senior ward staff members. It may take many weeks of meetings before the ideas inherent in the therapeutic milieu can be incorporated. Moreover, it may take time for ward staffs to learn what kinds of information are wanted. For instance, in one Weyburn Hospital ward of senile, bedridden men, one of us suddenly realized that there were just not enough staff members to feed the patients individually. Inquiry revealed that an attendant got one bowl of food and one spoon and went up and down the line thrusting food first into one mouth and then into the next. Because the attendants did not think anything could be done about the situation, they never mentioned it. Furthermore, as the doctors were responsible for the patients' physical health, years of accommodation to the situation had resulted in the attendants protecting the doctors' profes-

---

* The indiscriminate use of the patients' first names degrades their status. We are inclined to think that ward attendants should use them only if the patients are free to reciprocate. Some patients who are being rehabilitated from illnesses of long standing may badly need to relearn how to respond to their proper names and titles before leaving the hospital. Some defective, or very young, patients may have to be called by first names because of cultural attitudes or because of clinical reasons.

sional consciences by withholding such information. It was as if the attendants and the doctors had a complex system of reciprocity in which the attendants wore the mantle of "custodian" while, in exchange, the doctors agreed not to interfere with how the attendants exercised their custody.

Nurses and attendants in large hospitals have usually spent most of their time "controlling" difficult patients and giving care to helpless or chronic ones. This situation will have to be undermined without undermining the nurses themselves. For example, a nurse who feels that a patient must be tidy may believe it is perfectly all right to inspect a patient's bureau drawers. She will have to learn that the decision to be tidy is one that a patient must make for himself. It is in the discussion of such concrete and yet affect-laden issues that ideas are taught and learned. In our view, it is undesirable to "interpret" a nurse's desire for tidiness in such personality terms as compulsiveness or punitiveness. Indeed, *ad hominem* explanations are foreign to the whole philosophy of milieu therapy, which is founded upon the assumption that if staff members are taught to act appropriately toward patients then, through the experiences they undergo, the patients will come to feel appropriately. Most nurses and aides can learn that it is medically desirable for a patient to be tidy on his own initiative; then they can be taught how to encourage the patient to be so.

We say most nurses can be taught to do things in a new way, but some "old line" nurses find it impossible. They have been controlling patients and maintaining quiet, tidy wards for years, and they believe that the traditions of the hospitals where they learned these skills are sacred. In Weyburn Hospital we worked with a core of twenty men—senior ward supervisors and their Chief. As we have reported elsewhere, most of these men were delighted with the opportunity to create a more active program, but two of them and the Chief himself remained unconvinced and even were actively obstructive. The Chief finally resigned and the remaining two men were assigned to positions where they were in less contact with patients—but their loss was a serious, if temporary, blow to morale. We repeat, most nurses and aides are willing to change their actions if the changes seem feasible and if they can relate them to the patients' welfare.*

The problem of a patient who will not keep his personal effects in reasonable order now becomes one of who has the authority to teach him to want to be tidy. Usually, the answer is—the other patients. There are many ways in which such authority can be delegated to patients, but one of the more popular, at least in the United States, is to set up a government made up of the patients themselves. Since many excellent hospitals, especially in Continental Europe and Britain, do not have patient government, it may be a typically American innovation and peculiarly suitable to American hospitals. Perhaps for this reason alone it should be encouraged.

The first step in the actual formation of a patient government can be a meeting of the total patient group where a general invitation to comment upon the surroundings is given. In the beginning the meetings will almost certainly be silent and unproductive; later they will probably develop into "gripe" sessions. Nurses can be reminded at this stage that their purpose is to promote problem-focused patient interaction; they should try not to feel guilty,† and on no account should they feel that

---

* In another hospital, two nurses, who we thought were rather unlikely to learn new techniques, changed greatly when the teaching of milieu therapy was given to a senior nurse rather than to a psychiatrist.

† Some of the material produced by chronic patients is very poignant. One Weyburn Hospital patient who had been rehabilitated explained that while he was very ill and withdrawn, a nurse had explained gently to him that his brother had died, but that when the man who had sat next to him on a bench in the ward for ten years had died he had not even been taken to the funeral. He had felt much closer to this fellow patient than to the brother whom he had not seen for years. The hospital's entirely formal system of assigning importance to deaths was at fault.

they must defend the hospital to the patients. As the complaints increase, the patients can be invited to set up committees to consider what can be done about them. In this way the two basic kinds of problems emerge. First, there is the socio-emotional problem of getting along in the group in the first place; second, there is the instrumental problem of arriving at a consensus about what should be done and implementing the decision that is made. From the committees there should emerge a group of executive officers who will eventually be able to conduct ward meetings without the staff being present. It is of the utmost importance that the better integrated patients be included in all ward meetings from the start. If these less-ill patients are removed to attend to hospital routines or to go to other activities, the patient government will fail. The ward meetings should be treated as an important part of therapy, and their schedule should be inviolable.

Here we are discussing patient government in general. Large hospitals may have a government with representatives from all wards, but the important functional unit is the ward meeting. In such meetings all problems can be discussed, some can be solved, and ambiguities and obstructions that prevent solution can be dealt with.

Within the ward meeting itself, authority for different kinds of decisions varies. First, decisions about administrative necessities must be made by the ward administrator. There is no more point in pretending to share unshareable authority with patients and nurses than there is in refusing them authority they are well able to exercise. For example, the rules surrounding the holding of a patient on a court order must be made by the administration. In a different category is the authority for enforcing strongly held cultural norms that the patients and staff all share. For instance, rules about patients appearing seminude on the wards can be made by patients, staff, and ward administrator together, because the behavior violates generally held norms and concerns the reputation of the hospital as well as of the patients and staff. The patients themselves will almost always uphold these norms—in fact, if left to themselves, they usually will discipline one another more severely than staff members would.* Finally, the ground rules for living together on the ward should be left entirely in the hands of the patients. If patients make their own rules, they are very much more likely to live up to them. In this way, also, the informal social structure supports the formal rules. If rules are arbitrarily imposed upon patients, these rules will often be honored in the breach. In Kansas City, for example, where the patient group had considerable *esprit de corps,* an overweight patient was prescribed a diet by her doctor. He did not discuss it with her, and she was not interested in adhering to it. She was abetted by all the patients in getting extra food. If the patient herself had been considered in the initial decision, she might have been more willing to diet; if the other patients had been consulted about rules governing the giving of food to patients on diets, this subversion would have been less likely to take place.

Of course, there will always be some groups of patients who object to rules and want to change them; this is inevitable in a viable society and desirable in a therapeutic environment, but damaging subversion of the goals of the hospital can often be eliminated by allowing the patients to develop their own ways of reaching those goals wherever possible.

Many of the rules regarding housekeeping procedures can be made jointly between the ward administrator and the patient government. At Butler Hospital in Providence, Rhode Island,

---

* In some hospitals where patients are in contact with doctors a good deal of the time, there is an attempt to change the patients' attitudes toward modesty and prudery. We feel that there is confusion in some psychiatrists' minds about where differences in values leave off and pathology begins.

Robert Hyde * experimented with allowing patients to regulate their own medication. The patients were taught the use of prescribed drugs, were instructed concerning the drugs' outside limits, and were allowed to arrange their own dose within these limits.†

We have said that the ward meeting should include patients, ward staff, ward administrator, and a minimum of people from higher echelons. There are two reasons for keeping the number of senior people to a minimum: First, the decisions made on the ward are too concrete and specific for the people concerned with policy to join in regularly. Also, because attendance at these meetings uses their time wastefully and because they see the meeting out of context, it biases their view of the way policy is being acted out. Second, the tendency for discussion to reveal differences of opinion between members of echelons too far removed from each other creates ambiguity for everyone. The director and the policy-making echelons should keep a watchful eye on statistical and clinical evidences of the success or failure of the ward program, but they should not actively participate in ward meetings. It is, therefore, doubly important that the policy-making staff, in turn, meet among themselves—not only to reaffirm their goals and bring policy into line with them but also to make their own differences of opinion explicit and to find workable compromises. In the therapeutic milieu it is important that things be what they seem to be and that the authority delegated to patient government be unequivocal.

---

* In a personal communication to the authors.

† The possibilities in Hyde's move are pointed up by the fact that there are thousands of studies of the phenothiazine drugs but very few of them report whether or not the patients actually take the drugs. There is reason to believe that only about half the patients in chronic wards actually swallow the drugs they are given unless special pains are taken to see that they do. Many skillful ways of disposing of drugs have been recorded.

In a description of an early experiment, Robert Hyde and Harry Solomon [7] say:

In patient government the patients can:

1. Develop constitutional government with bylaws and regular meetings and elect officers to positions of leadership and responsibility which are recognized by both patients and hospital authorities. These leaders can assist the administration, occupational therapists, nurses, attendants and volunteer workers through consultation in planning and assignment of tasks.
2. Vote on complaints and suggestions and present them to the hospital authorities as the collective desire of the patient body rather than of one individual.
3. Organize and assign their own ward duties.
4. Recommend changes in ward rules.
5. Arrange, organize, conduct and assume responsibility for social activities.
6. Originate, plan and carry through a variety of special activity programs such as painting projects, mural paintings, writing and editing the hospital paper.
7. Form committees and elect leaders to engage in any program of hospital betterment approved by the hospital authorities.

Routine requests made by patient governments should be granted promptly or, if this is not possible, the delay should be promptly explained; patients probably should be able to obtain most of the things they request—but preferably through their own efforts. If the administration does not take their desires seriously, the patients will soon discover that patient government is a sham. Furthermore, the patients may resort to excessive demands in an attempt to test the real limits of an ambiguous situation. From the point of view of the therapeutic milieu, patient government offers a wide variety of everyday problems for solution.

A practical difficulty with patient government is that it always seems to be on the verge of efficiency only to miss achieving it because its top officers are discharged. This can be turned to account by encouraging the patients to have a large executive group; the shift in membership then gives the majority of the patients an opportunity to play both follower and leader roles in the course of their treatment. Staff members should remember that a certain amount of clumsiness is inevitable, and they must not dominate meetings in order to raise efficiency. Hyde and Solomon suggest having staff members rotate through the role of representative to patient government in order to avoid this pitfall. It is probably better, however, to restrict the staff role to the interpretation of reality and to the carrying of messages back and forth between the administration and the patients. If a staff member can learn to find more satisfaction in seeing a patient solve a problem than in solving it himself, he will have no difficulty in playing the representative role indefinitely. In our experience, new residents are often astonished at the variety of problems that patients can deal with themselves.

Patient government can take many forms but certain principles should be kept in mind. First, the patient government should make and enforce the majority of the ward rules; second, it should organize and execute the majority of the routine ward tasks; finally, no staff member should solve a problem if it can possibly be delegated to the patient group.

In spite of preparation, ward staff can react sharply to the increased autonomy that self-government brings to patients. Attendants who no longer need to control the patients can feel useless and demoralized. This can be avoided by starting to give them the new therapeutic role of assistant in problem solution *before* they lose their traditional role of keeper. Indeed, much discussion and activity can be based upon the role specifications of the aide. The ideal ward system is open in that new suggestions for role modifications are always welcome and are used as grist for the problem-solving mill.

In summary, authority in a hospital, day center, or clinic must be rationally allocated and democratic. Decision making must be flexible and "organic" in the sense that the people involved in the consequences of concrete decisions must have the authority to make them. This means that for therapeutic reasons, authority for making specific decisions should be delegated to patients and ward staff. This delegation breaks from the usual tradition of nursing and doctoring and brings its own problems, some of which we shall now discuss.

ABERRATIONS IN THE AUTHORITY STRUCTURE

In the course of allocating authority to the place where the therapeutic decisions must be made, problems arise.

The first kind of problem is quantitative and arises from an imbalance of authority at any particular level in the hierarchy. This can arise either from having too few "Indians" or too few "Chiefs." In most public facilities there are too few people with authority. In Weyburn Hospital, for example, we found not only too few doctors but also too few nurses and supervisors of rank and authority (Cumming and Cumming, "The Locus of Power in a Large Mental Hospital"). One of our first moves was to create a new echelon of nursing staff whose duties were to translate medical policy into ward operations and to carry back to the medical staff the problems the ward staff was facing.

There are hospitals that have too few members on their ward staff, but this may not be as serious as having too few policy makers. It is always possible to invent ways to use the less-impaired patients in therapeutic roles. The more serious implication of having too small a ward staff is that salaries do not meet the going rate—and then it is not only that staff members are too few but also that they are transient and therefore uncommitted to the job.*

---

* At the turn of the century there were accounts of "bug-housers" who appeared to have been psychopathic and alcoholic individuals and

If a hospital has too few upper-echelon people, many policy decisions are made informally on the ward and their consequences are never known. This is because sheer numbers keep the medical staff from being aware of what is happening from day-to-day—and it is this latter kind of knowledge upon which therapeutic milieu must always be built.

Some hospitals are weak at the top, not for lack of people but because of misplaced ideals of "permissiveness." Firm and unambiguous leadership seems essential in dealing with the mentally ill; the goal is to get the patients to solve their own problems, not to involve them in deciding the policy of the hospital. Charlotte Schwartz [9] has given a graphic account of the chaos resulting from a policy of permissiveness in the administration of a psychiatric ward in an exceptionally well-endowed hospital. It seems clear that both failure to exercise authority and failure to delegate it are anathema to the therapeutic milieu.

An important aspect of disordered authority is faulty communication—faulty in that it is either too much or too little. Too much communication, as we have indicated, is time wasting and can lead to doubts and misgivings, but too little is a far more serious and a more common disorder. Traditionally, the person nearest to a patient has the information most valuable for his treatment. Often in the face of changes that they do not understand, nurses and attendants will withhold this information and in this sense exercise an illegitimate power. Thomas Scheff [10] has shown that aides "train" new doctors to do things their way by withholding information from the doctors, and in Weyburn Hospital we found that information was a scarce and carefully guarded commodity.

---

who went from hospital to hospital. These people were described again and again, but it is hard to find anyone who has seen them. Our own experience is that most ward aides and attendants are stable, hard-working members of the community surrounding the hospital. In this connection, see Simpson's [8] descriptive studies of aides.

This process of controlling the wards through the with-holding of information is not always easy to see, because it be-comes embedded in the ongoing life of the hospital and ideologies tend to accumulate around it. For example, here is an excerpt from a dictated diary note made after one of our first staff meetings in Kansas City:

Dr. A. suggested that it might perhaps be a good idea if one of the doctors ate with the patients, and I supported this by citing the practice of the Medical Superintendent heading the table in the hospitals where moral treatment was practiced in the last century. Nursing reaction to this was quite sharp, and they seemed to feel that this would be both inappropriate and undesirable. This went on to an almost overt statement by Mrs. B. that doctors were not welcomed on the wards too much of the time. She seemed to be implying that if a doctor was on the ward, the patients would be bothering him all the time and would waste his time completely. Another nurse pointed out that the patients would get to know the doctors too well and would not respect them as much. Both of these nurses said that they were quite willing to protect the doctor from the continual demands of patients and that they could structure the situation so that the doctor would not be too much bothered. This led us to consider, after the meeting, the function of *not* having a doctor on the ward. The nurses seem to see an advantage in having the doctor as an authority figure, perceived as having great wisdom and power by the patients, and they do not wish to have the doctor shatter this image by interacting too much with the patients. The nurses are willing to do a lot of manipulating in order to see that this distance is maintained. Since this is rather a difficult thing to do, there must be a reason for it. The function that we impute to it, and that seems to have been almost stated in this meeting, is that the doctor's absence, plus his image, allows the nurses to invoke his authority in order to enforce their norms of ward behavior. In think-ing of this situation, other aspects occurred to us. For example, if a doctor can be persuaded to make rounds in a set fashion, and if he is introduced to the patients by the head nurse, the patients' idea that they must please the nurse in order to get to the doctor is re-inforced.

In this example, the stable group of ward nurses had formed a culture with working norms, an efficient communication system of their own, and a reservoir of power to control the ward, partly by withholding information. This situation had arisen largely because the nurses had not been delegated the legitimate authority that they needed in order to operate their wards efficiently. Allocation of such authority did much to open the ward to the doctor and thus, paradoxically, to make the nurses more amenable to him. Allocation of more legitimate authority to the nurses had gone a long way toward solving this problem.

The structure of authority can fall into difficulties through qualitative distortions. This happens when authority is vested in the wrong role or is unevenly allocated. Jules Henry [11] has described a situation in which nurses tried to operate wards when they had two separate and contradictory lines of authority bearing down on them. This can also happen in hospitals when the nurse is reponsible both to the training office and to the nursing office. It happens more dramatically in the more complex situation when she must satisfy both a nursing office—which in turn is responsible to a medical director who is allied to the business manager—and a doctor who is responsible to a clinical director. Conflicting lines of authority make it impossible for a therapeutic community to exist because one authority must be appeased at the expense of the other and every second decision ends in frustration. For the therapeutic milieu to function, there must be a straight line of authority from the ward to the clinical director—it is for him to mediate with other branches of the structure, through the medical director if necessary.

This type of divided authority can produce not only paralysis but disturbance. Stanton and Schwartz have described (in *The Mental Hospital*) the principle of "triangulation" in which two staff members who were at loggerheads over the handling of a patient expressed their frustrations in such a way as to create profound distress in the patient. This infliction of problems upon a patient may be a flaw either in the authority structure or in the communication system.

Similar authority problems can occur in clinics where the upper echelons are in the majority and can create, formally and informally, the culture necessary for their therapeutic goals. However, small groups of highly trained people working together are prey to a different disorder—factionalism. In some cases "schools" develop and the result is two parallel institutions—one perhaps using drugs to treat depressions and the other eschewing them as an "assault on the patient." This results in a few unfortunate underlings serving two masters. Although factionalism is a different type of structural split, it is essentially the same thing that both Jules Henry and Stanton described— that is, the depredations of a divided authority no matter whether the rift is formal or informal.

Another qualitative distortion of authority occurs when the various disciplines are not adequately represented at different levels of the hierarchy. Most commonly the aide—who knows the most about the patient—is not heard in the policy-making echelons; but other problems can also arise. In one small hospital in which we have worked, the medical hierarchy appeared to lack a level. The senior physicians were absorbed in practicing and teaching psychotherapy. The wards were administered by residents who, in the course of their work, heard the problems and complaints of the nurses and patients. However, these residents had no representation in the staff conference. An interested staff representative was needed to advise the residents and to speak for the ward at senior staff meetings. Such an intervening echelon would have improved the functioning of both the administration and the wards.

This kind of deficit in the authority structure can lead to the communication problem known as "skipping." It is often more effective to go directly to the chief than to the person to whom one is officially responsible—especially if the latter is incompletely qualified for his role or if it is unclear that he is really in authority. It is easier, too, for the chief to entertain a complaint and "hear both sides" separately than to send the complainer back through channels. Skipping will occur, of course. Even in the military a soldier has the right to take his complaint to a higher officer upon notification of those in the chain of command. In less formal organizations, however, this etiquette frequently breaks down. Nevertheless, the authority holder should always be alert for skipping and should try to divert communication back through the correct channels. If skipping becomes a pattern, the authority structure needs inspection and possibly alteration. Persistent skipping almost always demoralizes the person skipped—first, because it cuts him out of the communication stream and, second, because it gives presumptive equality to those under him who, by other criteria such as salary and training, are not his equal.

These distorted communication patterns, such as too much communication and administration by "permissiveness," are the pathologies of small hospitals and clinics. Where staff numbers are low and where the climate is suffused with therapeutic ideas, there is a temptation to forget task orientation and to administer in a quasi-therapeutic style or perhaps in a way reminiscent of a family or a group of peers. This leads to an undercutting of authority, to a failure to confront disagreements, and to a demoralization of those staff members whose duty it is to keep records, see that things get done on time, and generally attend to the businesslike side of things. In such systems it is not uncommon for a head nurse or the administrator's secretary to be known as "punitive," "aggressive," or "sick." When she finally retires or leaves, there is a general sigh of relief, followed by dismay when her successor "changes" overnight and assumes the unloved role of instrumental leader. To attempt to administer a working situation in a quasi-therapeutic way almost always ends in someone's avoiding the responsibility of telling people to do unpleasant things. Sometimes the unpleasant tasks are foisted onto people who are then scapegoated for their activities. Authority should probably always be exercised in appropriate roles and openly—never disguised as comradeship, particularly at the top of the system; ambiguities at the top can resonate throughout the entire structure.

Structural deficits lead to malfunction of the system, but the malfunction can also occur because of abrogation of authority. When a doctor says, "I hate to run a ward because of all the red tape," he is saying, "I do not like to take authority over things I consider nonmedical." Unfortunately, when authority is abrogated, it is always usurped. In many hospitals the nurses have much longer tenure than the doctors and they slowly accumulate authority that doctors give up. When an attempt is made to restore this authority to the doctors, the nurses defend their right to it on the ground of tradition. Nurses say: "When you have been here as long as I have you'll see that this is the only way to do it." Sometimes abrogated authority is taken back by energetic doctors. In Weyburn Hospital, before our time, such a doctor had managed to create a "total push" ward in spite of the apathy of the administration.[12] When this doctor left, the ward reverted to its former inert condition, and many of the attendants he had worked with reached the glum conclusion that all such efforts were fated to end in regression. If the doctor had found it possible to establish a firm authority for the people who would remain after he had left, the improvement would probably have persisted.

Sometimes the authority of doctors is more seriously usurped. In Weyburn Hospital at one time, as we have described previously, the greatest power was abrogated to the business office. There were several reasons for this: First, the business manager and his staff had control of valuable and scarce goods and services which they used as a kind of patronage. Second, doctors had abrogated much of their authority. Third, the business manager was able to invoke, in support of his withholding tactics, the book-balancing and profit-making norms appropriate to quite different bureaucracies such as factories and banks.* In many years, in spite of the privations caused by a budget of about three dollars per patient per day, the business office was able to declare a surplus. (It is a rare hospital indeed that uses as an index of its efficiency the cost per patient returned to the community.) The business manager shared his power † with the senior nurses, and it was clear that literally nothing could be done if he and they did not approve it. Impulses toward improvement started by doctors or imaginative and compassionate summer-relief attendants wore themselves out against the stone wall of the business office. The hospital was a graveyard of unused talents. Weyburn Hospital was at that time unexceptional in the authority exercised by the business office. Ivan Belknap [13] described situations from a hospital in the United States that matched it in many details, and British doctors have told us of almost identical situations.

In attacking this most common authority problem of large hospitals, it is probably wisest to subdivide the business manager role so that it is composed of several functionally specific parts. Thus, instead of having one person oversee all the business aspects of the hospital, different people may be assigned to procure commodities, to dispense services, and to maintain accounts. The business manager has essentially an adjutant's role. Since he himself cannot make therapeutic decisions, and

---

* Hospitals share this problem with schools, universities, and other "collectivity oriented" and nonprofit organizations.

† There are many ways of telling at first glance how much power a business manager has in a hospital. One of the easiest is to look at the parking lot. The best space is usually marked "Medical Director," and the next best, "Business Manager."

since in a hospital all decisions should be made with their therapeutic impact in mind, the business manager must primarily function as a source of information. When policy decisions are being made, it is the responsibility of the business manager to know the state of the budget, to know the cost of the various goods and services the hospital must buy, and to present these facts to the policy makers. A good business manager is adept at circumventing situations wherein only one of two important alternatives can be chosen. His efficiency, like everyone's, should be judged in terms of the patient's welfare, never in terms of whether or not he has a budgetary surplus.*

Authority can be usurped by informal groupings whose goals are the opposite of the formal goals of the system, but in the end authority must be validated by the people who carry out orders. As we have said, if an officer tells his troops to march and they do not, there is little his authority alone can do to make them unless he invokes power through the threat of disciplinary measures. Their willingness to march gives his office its authority. The problem of getting the ward staffs to want to do what the policy makers tell them they must do is basically a question of developing a ward culture with the same goals and values as the policy makers' own. This will be discussed in detail in Chapter 8, but it is well to realize that all the planning in the world will not make authority effective if that authority's validation is lacking.

EGO RESTITUTION AND AUTHORITY

What does the allocation of authority contribute to the ego-building process? First, it supplies a continuously un-

---

* In fairness, it should be said that boards of directors and government departments in their concern for saving money may often hire business managers considerably more capable than the medical superintendents. This, however, only exacerbates the situation and in no real sense causes it. Even a weak superintendent can manage if he is supported by an authority structure planned for therapeutic goals.

ambiguous and reliable social structure that does not create adventitious anxiety. A clear authority structure allows a patient to address himself to the functional anxiety of problem solution and, thus, to act in numerous roles, to build ego sets, and to exercise ego ability. Second, authority structure provides a patient with problems to solve. There are two basic reasons for avoiding false egalitarianism, spurious democratic process, and, above all, quasi-paternalism. First, patients have difficulty enough in retaining perceptual clarity without this fortuitous ambiguity being added, and, second, patients must have a chance to solve genuine problems of authority. This means that the consequences of patients' decisions not only affect their hospital lives but have meaning for their post-hospital careers. The seemingly small matter of orderliness on the ward can be, in this sense, a major therapeutic issue with important implications for the patient's autonomy, competency, and ability to cooperate. All these ego abilities are building blocks for successful life outside the hospital. For men, the question of deciding that they have the obligation to handle the matter of tidiness themselves is vital; for women, the effect of orderliness upon others may become more clear. Similarly, a discussion and resolution of appropriate modesty can be used to develop toleration of differences—perhaps through learning for the first time to recognize other people's strongly held values. There are many other kinds of authority problems that can be solved on the wards or in the day center and some of the more important are concerned with work; these are so important, in fact, that we shall return to them repeatedly in discussing other aspects of the milieu. It will suffice to say here that patient government has many of the aspects of work. In participating in it the patient can learn new ego organizations or reinstate old ones; he can acquire identity feeling in an unambiguous situation that has bearing on his future life. He may be able to improve his concept of himself through consistently meeting the expectations of those around him. He is helped in this by the support of other patients and by becoming deeply enough involved with his environment to learn it well and thus to use it for problem solution.

One of the more important reasons for an unambiguous authority structure is that it gives the patient a chance to act in clearly differentiated roles with clearly allocated tasks. Such role differentiation, in turn, should allow him to differentiate his ego organizations in such a way as to give him a greater clarity of perception and a greater decisiveness in action. For patients suffering from the disorders of ego development—especially spreading—these effects of an unambiguous authority structure should, if our theory approaches reality, be doubly important.

Interaction creates sentiments among people, and these are usually solidary sentiments. Therefore, a set of normative expectations will usually develop quite rapidly on a ward, and the average patient will, through the pressure of his peers, learn to honor them and in some part recover his social skills. However, there are almost always patients who cannot or will not join the patients' society. With forbearance and effort, these strains can be used to advantage by persistently returning them to the patient group as problems in human understanding or in authority and control. There will be disappointments, especially when improvement is slow, but on the whole most patients will benefit remarkably from this kind of program.

Problems of authority, then, like problems of the physical milieu, are special cases of solving the puzzle of living in society. In the next chapter we shall consider role relationships in the therapeutic milieu and their relationship to problem solving and ego restitution.

References

[1] JOINT COMMISSION ON MENTAL ILLNESS AND HEALTH, *Action for Mental Health* (New York: Basic Books, 1961).

[2] CHESTER BARNARD, *The Functions of the Executive* (Cambridge, Mass.: Harvard University Press, 1938).

[3] MAX WEBER, "Three Types of Legitimate Rule," *Wirtschaft und Gesellschaft* (Tübingen, Germany: J. C. B. Mohr, 1956).

[4] AMITAI ETZIONI, "Interpersonal and Structural Factors in the Study of Mental Hospitals," *Psychiatry,* 23 (February 1960), 13.

[5] L. GARCIA-BUENULL, "The Clarinda Plan" (paper read to the 89th Annual Meeting of the APHA, Detroit, 1961).

[6] GEORGE HOMANS, *The Human Group* (New York: Harcourt, Brace, 1950).

[7] ROBERT W. HYDE and HARRY C. SOLOMON, "Patient Government: A New Form of Group Therapy," *Digest of Neurology and Psychiatry,* No. XVIII (April 1950).

[8] RICHARD L. SIMPSON, *Attendants in American Mental Hospitals* (publication of the Institute for Research in Social Science, the University of North Carolina, Chapel Hill, N. C.).

[9] CHARLOTTE SCHWARTZ, "Problems for Psychiatric Nurses in Playing a New Role on a Mental Hospital Ward," in M. Greenblatt,

D. J. Levinson, and R. H. Williams (eds.), *The Patient and the Mental Hospital* (Glencoe, Ill.: Free Press, 1957), 402-426.

[10] THOMAS J. SCHEFF, "Control over Policy by Attendants in Mental Hospitals," *Journal of Health and Human Behavior*, 2 (Summer 1961), 93.

[11] JULES HENRY, "The Formal Social Structure of a Psychiatric Hospital," *Psychiatry*, XVII, 2 (1954), 139.

[12] DEREK H. MILLER, "The Rehabilitation of Chronic Open-Ward Neuropsychiatric Patients," *Psychiatry*, XVII, 4 (1954), 347.

[13] IVAN BELKNAP, *Human Problems of a State Mental Hospital* (New York: McGraw-Hill, 1956).

CHAPTER 7

Roles and Role Relationships

In any organization the structuring of role relationships affects the efficiency with which goals are reached. In the therapeutic milieu it not only facilitates the job of the doctor, nurse, and aide, but it *is* in itself the raw material of therapy inasmuch as the acting out of the patient role in complement to the roles of the others in the environment is the road to ego restitution. Therefore, the content and boundaries of all the roles in the therapeutic environment must be carefully thought out. First, however, we must state a general principle of the allocation of the content of roles, without which the therapeutic milieu probably will not work: *Every task that can be organized and performed by patients should be considered for allocation to them—this is the grist for the mill of problem solution. Only when patients must seek help in planning or facilitating should they turn to the aide, and he in turn must do all that he possibly can before turning to the nurse, and so on up to the medical administrator.* In this way problems of everyday living in the hospital or day center—and in some cases the home—can be put to maximum use. If doctors begrudge nurses tasks that

137

they think are medical, and nurses are jealous of the content of the nursing role, then the aides also will believe that their status depends upon holding onto role content, and the result will be the traditional hospital in which the upper members of the hierarchy are so busy that they "cannot possibly serve all the patients" and in which the patients are perfectly idle.

The retention of decision-making authority at a high level in the structure is usually justified on the grounds that aides are not equipped to make therapeutic decisions. Yet it is obvious that aides, by the nature of their work, constantly have to make decisions affecting patients' lives. The traditional system allows an aide to make decisions; it merely makes it almost impossible for these decisions to be therapeutic. This is because ego therapy requires action, and if an aide has to appear *not* to be making decisions, action must be kept to a minimum. The therapeutic milieu, however, requires that the roles at the lowest level in the hospital hierarchy be overtly defined as therapeutic, decision-making roles. It is hard for doctors and nurses to take this seriously. In Kansas City, for example, the nurses were loath to give up their ironclad rule that the patients take a shower every morning, even though they truly believed that the patients should learn to organize and run their own lives.

The therapeutic milieu defines the patient as actor, initiator, cooperator, and manager of his own affairs and everyone else as assistants in this process. This is its most important single difference from traditional treatment where the patient is the passive recipient of help. The nature of the damaged ego, in our view, demands that the patient be primarily actor, not recipient. It may, of course, take more staff time to encourage a patient to act independently than it would to take action on his behalf. However, this is the purpose of staff time. It takes a nurse longer to encourage a patient to be at breakfast on time, but if she makes his bed for him instead of urging him to do so himself, she retards his recovery. Furthermore, although she does it in the name of saving time, she is probably acting to spare herself tension. The familiar phrase "It takes less time to do it myself" often means "I cannot stand the frustration of seeing it done inefficiently." Whether there is a loss or a gain of staff time is secondary to having patients look after themselves.

We shall briefly describe some of the chief characteristics of the key roles in a hospital or day center, discuss the relationships among them, and suggest some of the conflicts that can arise. The roles of the members of out-patient clinic teams will be discussed later. This is because the clinic, treating patients on an out-patient basis, is a much more integral part of the community than the hospital and is open to different pressures and different temptations.

THE MEDICAL DIRECTOR AND HIS BOARD

It has been a theme of this book that every agency provided by society for the support and control of its deviant members has two goals. This duality endows the Director of such an agency with a Janus role, in which he must face both toward society and toward the patient. Furthermore, he is structurally at the boundary, meeting and planning with board members as well as with his own staff. He must represent the hospital to society and society to the patients and those members of the staff who are "on the patient's side."

The Medical Director must be qualified to provide an intelligent stewardship for the money that his hospital costs. He must be medically trained so that the principle of safeguarding the interests of the patient will be deeply instilled. In the conflict between society and patient, the cards are stacked on society's side so that the Director must lean well over toward the patient in order to remain upright. Finally, the Director must understand administration sufficiently well to run an institution by delegating his authority to those who are "for the patient." He should be aware that every decision he makes has an influence on the whole milieu, and therefore he should be able to analyze the *nature and direction* of the change that will result from any given action.

This is a difficult role, and to perform it adequately the Medical Director must be able to act within an appropriate administrative structure. Once policy is established, the Director should be entitled to a security in carrying it out. It should be understood that he will sometimes oppose his Board in order to safeguard the interests of his patients, and occasionally he will have to oppose staff members who forget that the purpose of the hospital is to expel its members and not to form a permanent subculture.

The Medical Director cannot fulfill his function adequately if he is liable to removal from his position at the whim of an elected representative. Direct political control of mental hospitals has been a curse to patient care in America and is surely one of the major contributing factors to our low hospital standards. However, in Britain, although the Medical Director has been separated from political influence entirely, his Business Manager reports directly to the Board of Control at the same time that he is subject to the Medical Director's decision on internal matters. Consequently, the Business Manager often finds it easy to adopt the point of view of his fellow laymen and to oppose the Medical Director. Neither of these situations seems desirable—the Medical Director should be protected by the equivalent of Civil Service status from capricious political action, but he should remain the sole responsible agent between the hospital and society.

Besides security in his position, the well-trained Medical Director should be entitled to a statement of policy setting forth the purposes of the hospital and establishing priorities among them. Priorities are indicators of the kinds of compromises the Director will have to make in order to reach his own goals. If the Board places great value upon the prize herd of swine, the Director will be warned that his therapeutic endeavors will have to take second place to the fluctuating needs of the pigs.

Once established, policy is an important support to the Director. First, it helps him to be objective, because policy is a corrective against expediency, influence, personal preferences, and narrow viewpoints. Second, the Director's ability to relate unpopular decisions to policy is an important defense against his critics.

The Medical Director must have authority commensurate with his responsibility, and the Board must delegate it to him unequivocally. Furthermore, once having delegated it, the Board must always use the Director as an intermediary when they act in regard to hospital affairs. They must never hear complaints either from inside or outside the hospital without the Director's knowledge, and at no time should they reverse the Director's decisions. The Director must always be allowed either to reverse his own decision or to resign if he cannot persuade the Board to his view.

Trust and consideration on the part of the Board imposes certain duties on the Director. First, he must inform the Board regularly about the affairs of the hospital and apprise them of his plans. He must report immediately any incident that seems likely to arouse public protest, and he must communicate both his successes and failures. If he does not, he encourages the Board to develop informal patterns of obtaining information, and thus he breaks down his working relationship with society's agent.

The Medical Director will do well to encourage the people to whom he is responsible and the public in general to make regular visits in both informal groups and in duly constituted committees, so that they have an investment in the progress of the hospital. He will be wise, also, to encourage the press to keep the public acquainted with new developments and reminded of the over-all goal of his program, so that temporary setbacks can be understood and treated calmly.

The Medical Director must never separate the administrative and clinical supervision of the hospital; the administrative decision must always be in the service of the clinical, and both must be a facet of policy. Thus, the Medical Director is the agent through whom social policy reaches the hospital. If the public's humane intentions become lost, the Director is ultimately to blame.

The biggest pitfall for the Medical Director of a large hospital is that of undertaking to be the keeper of the public purse. In many hospitals, as Belknap has pointed out in *Human Problems of a State Mental Hospital,* the Director has his main contacts with his Business Manager and the Chief Attendant. As a rule, the latter two share society's fear and devaluation of the mentally ill and also its book-balancing orientation. In such hospitals the doctors are usually set apart and without influence—to be tolerated by a Director who knows that the more energetic they are the sooner they will leave in frustration. The Medical Director, then, should at all times keep his doctors in first place; his primary bond in the hospital should be with the medical staff to whom he delegates his therapeutic authority and in whose activities he keeps an encouraging but critical interest. Although the doctors act on his behalf in the therapeutic milieu, the Director remains the leader of the medical team, and the success of the program depends upon his commitment to its goals.

DOCTORS

Psychiatrists find it hard to learn their role in the therapeutic milieu because it differs from the roles of individual therapist and medical doctor. There is a striking difference between the medical role in the general hospital and in the psychiatric hospital. In the former, the doctor is really a consultant. He gets his authority by courtesy of the hospital—and that means, for most practical purposes, from the nursing hierarchy. This authority is legitimated through the doctor's special training. He is not "in the line" and cannot really give orders except through the nursing staff. In the psychiatric hospital, however, where the doctor is a member of the line of authority, he must take responsibility for the patients' total welfare, and that involves administrative duties far beyond direct medical care. Some of these duties can be branded as custodial or controlling. Under these circumstances, doctors often abrogate their routine responsibilities to people of lower rank and then stigmatize these staff members as custodial or punitive. The doctors, in such situations, do not realize that they themselves have created the situation in which the tasks they did not want were done in ways they did not like. This tacit criticism of the shifting of routine responsibilities sounds as if it were contradictory to our governing principle of allowing everything to be done as far down the hierarchy as possible, but it is not. The doctor need not actually *do* the tasks he rejects, but he must take responsibility for their being done, and being done in a way that maximizes their therapeutic potential. For example, in Weyburn Hospital, at the beginning of our stay, we discovered that there was not enough soap to maintain sanitary conditions. When we tried to get more we found that we had no effective administrative control of the ward and that we were dealing with people whose standards and values about the running of the wards were quite different from our own. We had to make the choice of assuming administrative responsibility for the stock of soap on the ward or of accepting the standards of "enough soap" that already existed in the hospital. The frustration we met at this point was that our professional qualifications no longer legitimated our authority. We found that only decisions unequivocally concerned with life or death were really authoritative. When we tried to legitimate our right to demand more soap by virtue of our medical qualifications, we found ourselves up against a morass of reasons—against which we could not argue because we did not know enough—of why there was a scarcity of soap. Briefly, we had to get into the line of authority and run our wards or be powerless ornaments necessary only for prescribing drugs and writing death certificates but encouraged, for appearances sake, to give psychotherapy to a few selected patients.

Not only must the doctor undertake a new kind of administrative role but, as leader of a therapeutic team, he must enter a new relationship with the nurses. If he comprehends that it is the daily activity of the patients among themselves, the aides, and the nurses that restores them to health, the doctor will understand how important it is to be able to communicate his intentions to the nurses. For this, he must have more access to their ideas and thinking than he is accustomed to. Furthermore, in most mental hospitals the doctor has a large number of patients assigned to him. If he is going to have any impact on their lives, he must work through nurses, and nurses in turn must work through aides. To start this process going, the doctor must believe that nurses have a therapeutic potential. It is curious how many doctors believe that nurses can inflict great psychological harm on patients, and only doctors can benefit them. In most hospitals both the doctor and his staff are powerless without the other; the nurse or aide has an immense amount of knowledge of the patients, but the doctor has a theoretical framework for ordering that knowledge effectively. To get a free flow of information between himself and the nurse, the doctor must be prepared to enter her world.

The world of the nurse and the aide in the mental hospital is intimately tied up with the world of the patient. Traditionally, much of the nurse's work is concerned with housekeeping. This means that she must supervise ward cleaning, procure clothing, and arrange to have window glass repaired and plumbing serviced. She must serve meals and take patients back and forth to eat them. This is the custodial side of hospital life that the doctor repudiates, but if he is going to enter the world of the nurse, he must find it in his heart to be interested in it.

The prototype of the therapeutic team at work is the ward meeting in which the problems of the day are discussed and analyzed and decisions about actions are made. The doctor's wider perspective, his greater control of theory, and his access to resources make him indispensable to nurses—once they are convinced that he defines their day-to-day activities as the *sine qua non* of the therapeutic process.

THE PSYCHIATRIC NURSE

The nurse is in contact with the patients more than the doctor is, and she is, in one sense, the keystone of the therapeutic structure. Nurses know this. In Kansas City, a midwinter blizzard once kept every doctor snowbound, but the nurses and aides all appeared, and most of them on time. The task of developing the therapeutic milieu is largely to exploit this central role of the nurse to the utmost.

In general medicine the nurse appears to have three kinds of activities. First, there are medical treatments that the doctor delegates to her. When she starts an intravenous feeding, for example, she can be thought of as the doctor's agent, doing for him an essential medical task. Second, there are those things that a nurse does and a doctor never does but that he specifically prescribes; for instance, he may tell the nurse that his patient has a circulatory disorder and needs special nursing care to prevent bedsores. Finally, there is a body of nursing skills that the doctor never even comments on. He never says: "Be careful when you move my patient because you may hurt him—he has just had an operation." This is the nurse's lore—the content of her role that is complementary to the doctor's role—and he would never dream of invading it. It is taught to nurses by other nurses and is the ground upon which they stand.

In psychiatry, however, the situation is by no means so clear. A resident who had successfully rehabilitated a ward of eighty severely regressed chronic schizophrenics [1] once told us: "I know nothing about treating schizophrenia but I know a lot about nursing it." * He had successfully learned from nurses and aides what could be done in the course of intimate daily contact with schizophrenics to restore them to more nearly normal patterns of behavior. This attitude is reminiscent of the moral treatment of the nineteenth century—probably the most important antecedent of milieu therapy.

Nursing is first of all an action-oriented profession and for this reason is particularly useful to ego-damaged patients. If nurses can learn to use their skills *in cooperation with* patients rather than *on* them, they are in a good position to help the patients toward ego restitution.

Psychiatric practice, with its emphasis upon the verbal interchange and the production of insight, has directed our attention away from action as a central form of treatment. Furthermore, the belief that mental illness is an essentially intrapsychic condition, probably arising in early life traumata, leads to the inference that it can only be treated in a circumstance similar to that in which it occurred—namely, the transference situation. When psychiatric nurses and aides have been able to make the incontinent patient continent and the mute patient speak, this has been looked upon as "readying the patient for treatment," with the implication that this is merely a transitory improvement masking the "real" pathology beneath. This concern with psychoanalytic treatment has distracted attention from the development of a body of specific nursing skills that can effect progressive improvements in the

---

* See in this regard the work of Orlando.[2]

day-to-day behavior of large numbers of mentally ill patients.

Although psychoanalysts themselves are often indifferent to the personality of the nurse, some of the derived therapies emphasize the importance of selecting nurses by strict criteria. It is our observation that nurses and aides vary greatly in both personality and motivation and that there will never be a time when they are so plentiful that they can be selected by personality tests—supposing that such tests were trustworthy. Therefore, the role must be structured so that good patient care can be given by the average people who are available to give it. Nevertheless, certain characteristics are desirable; we shall digress briefly here to describe what we think to be the basic characteristics of the good psychiatric nurse, or aide, and the minimum skills which she should bring to her role.

Anyone who nurses an ego-damaged patient should be able to communicate her own thoughts to her patient in simple and unambiguous terms and be able to pick up the nuances of meaning in ordinary interaction. Beyond this, it is desirable that the nurse should live in a relatively complex situation herself. For example, membership in a family or a stable friendship group suggests that the nurse will be relatively normative and thus capable of forming a solidary group with her fellow nurses. Furthermore, membership in some community organization can be evidence of ego complexity and of energy and might suggest that the nurse will be able to assume the role of leader to the patient. As we said in Chapter 2, full membership in adult society is necessary for anyone who undertakes to socialize the young or restore the deviant to normal functioning.

It is often said that the psychiatric nurse should have "empathy." It is assumed here that most people have sufficient empathy to deal with patients when they are trained how to do it. It is probably more important that they have energy enough to keep interacting with the patients even when they get a very low response from them. Indeed, overempathic persons may be much disadvantaged in dealing with the mentally ill. The housemother of a successful halfway house that we visited was characterized by a kind of even vigor and cheerfulness that persisted in spite of a level of feedback so low that it might have tried a more "empathic" person.

Nurses ideally need, besides membership in a normatively governed society of their own, humanity, energy, and spontaneity. None of these qualities can be taught, but they can be rewarded and encouraged. We once saw a patient throw a glass of lemonade at an aide. The aide impulsively picked up the pitcher and set out in pursuit of the patient who had turned and run away. By the time the aide caught the patient, the ridiculous side of the scene had overcome her and she burst into laughter. The patient laughed too, and they returned together to the dining room. It is doubtful if an ability to analyze the patient's aggression and the aide's own feelings about it would have accomplished as much. Some knowledge of cultural anthropology, however, seems likely to help nurses and aides become tolerant of a wide range of behavior. Furthermore, this knowledge does so without raising the self-doubt and anxiety that teaching psychoanalytic principles so often does.

There is another very important reason why aides and nurses should not look at the patients through psychoanalytic eyes. If the patient is to repair his ego in a useful way, he should be on the receiving end of all kinds of different role interactions. If everyone with whom the patient interacts mirrors back to him the same facet of his ego, he will be retrained in too narrow an environment. He should be learning to interact with people who view him differently. This does not mean *inconsistently,* but complementarily. In this connection, Dr. Rudolph Freudenberg, Medical Director of Netherne Hospital, South Coulsdon, England, told us that the patients on the most heterogeneous wards make the greatest improvements. The development of new ego sets and organizations and the clear differentiation among them seems to us to be much more likely if they are role holders with clearly different points of view and different modes of interacting, reflecting back to the patient different but consistent aspects of himself. Thus, a doctor may reflect back to the patient some parts of the patient's character and personality that have their roots in his early history, a social worker may interact with him as a man who is a husband and father, but the ward staff may know him *primarily* as a truck driver temporarily out of work and in the hospital. In this way the patient can reintegrate himself in all his aspects—the more immediate with the more remote—and perhaps reorganize his ego in more complex ways.

To return to the nurse and what she should know, we might say that given the minimum characteristics we have described, the nurse might ideally be taught the characteristics of the common forms of ego damage. It should not be necessary, for example, that every psychiatrist should prescribe for every schizophrenic patient that he wear his own clothes, be called by his proper name, and be continually reminded of his status and identity. Every psychiatric nurse should know that the schizophrenic will have difficulty handling his impulses acceptably and will need patience and tolerance while he is regaining control.

The nurse should be taught to run a ward meeting. She should also be able to develop minor, practical problem-solving situations and organize groups of patients to attack them. She should watch for signs of discouragement and learn that help, rewards, and consolations must be offered only when the patient appears to need them in order to persist. Throughout the problem-solving process the nurse should be prepared to offer information and "structure" by reminding the patients of their own ground rules as well as the hospital requirements. This should be done in a friendly and unambiguous way. A good psychiatric nurse or aide never *hints*.

A nurse should know that problems should be relevant to the patient's life pattern, and she should be able to invent ways of solving them that are appropriate to it. This means that the nurse respects the patients' standards and values because she has been taught enough about subcultures to tolerate a variety of habits and beliefs. She should know, for example, the results of studies such as Mark Zborowski's [3] in which response to pain is seen to vary greatly among different ethnic groups.

The nurse must, of course, be competent in her own routine instrumental tasks because this sets the example of competence for the patients. She must be taught to work closely with her own colleagues, for this at once preserves her from overinvolvement with patients and provides the patients with the chance to be members of a normal working group and thus muster ego organizations of great practical utility.

In the hospital or day center where nurses are in relative predominance, they will work directly with the patients. In hospitals where the nurse has a supervisory role, she must also have the ability to organize and evaluate the work of the aide and his patient group and to assist the aide when the situation becomes too complex for one person to handle. She must, at the same time, maintain her orientation to physical medicine and act as eyes, ears, and occasionally brain for the doctor in the detection and evaluation of illness. The supervising nurse can take on many tasks that are routinely thought of as the work of physicians, since much of her own routine will be taken over by aides. She can, for instance, answer letters from relatives, interview visitors, supervise drug programs within prescribed limits, and initiate new physicians into the workings of the hospital. If this sounds utopian, it should be remembered that most nurses, especially in large hospitals, have much more ability than they have been encouraged to use. For example, in some state hospitals a doctor will go to a ward and ask a nurse or aide what to say in a letter to a patient's relative and then return to his office and dictate the letter, thus doubling the time needed for the task.

Although many such concrete tasks can contribute to a therapeutic milieu, others create strains in the nurse's role. One of these is record keeping. Although certain records are necessary for legal and clinical reasons, such things as writing daily nursing notes that nobody reads and keeping linen inventories that are duplicated in the laundry are a tremendous drain on nursing time. A continuing committee including all levels of medical and nursing staff should maintain an ongoing review of the records being kept and their purpose. Decreased record keeping frees the nurse to be with the patients.

When a nurse has a repertoire of many kinds of skills for treating the mentally ill, she will not be "custodial" or "punitive" toward the patients. In Ville Evrard Hospital in Paris we once watched a recreational therapist take a group of very passive schizophrenic patients and, by exhortation and gentle positioning, form them into a ring. Then, placing himself in the center of the ring, he began to toss a basketball in turn to each patient. If the patient caught it, the therapist called upon him to return it. If the patient failed to raise his hands to catch the ball, the therapist took the ball, placed the patient's hands on it to indicate what was expected, and then called upon him to return it. If the patient caught the ball and returned it, the therapist reacted with pleasure. When all the patients had caught and returned the ball, the therapist drew one patient into the center and took his place in the circle. From here the therapist began to direct the ball in more and more intricate patterns, thus forcing the patients' attention to the total group. When the game seemed in danger of becoming monotonous, the therapist selected two patients and gave them a rope to hold between them about six inches from the floor. Next he took the hand of the patient next to him, encouraged that patient to take the hand of his neighbor, and led the group in a slow trot around the small gymnasium and finally over the rope with a little jump. Then he split the single line of patients into two, and first one line and then the other jumped the rope. Next, people from each line came alternately to the rope and returned to their own line. These simple rhythms force the patient into a greater awareness of himself and of those around him. For the nurse, the activity is the exercise of a professional skill and the reward is its success.

A persistent problem for the nurse is the maintenance of the functional specificity of her role. Because the therapeutic process involves working with patients in everyday situations, it tends to be reminiscent of the activities that families and friends perform together. However, for her own as well as the patients' protection, the nurse must keep her specific role clear.

There is a case to be made for giving "care to the whole man," but there are theoretical grounds for doubting whether this concept is adequate for modern psychiatric nursing practice. In order to discuss this important point adequately, we shall return for a moment to a discussion of the doctor's role. Talcott Parsons, in his discussion of medical practice, has suggested that one of the most important sources of strain between the doctor and the patient is the dependent relationship that tends to grow up. The patient would like the doctor to abandon his specific healing role and take on a more diffuse role of comforter and personal friend. If the doctor yields, he ceases to be a specialist interested only in the patient's health and becomes interested in *all* the needs and desires of the patient. If the relationship is fully diffuse, the doctor finds he cannot deny the patient's wishes without justifying himself as he would with members of his family. This is an untenable relationship for a doctor, and this is the reason for the refusal of many medical men to treat their families and for their reluctance to treat their friends.

Of all the specialists, psychiatrists probably grant the most diffuse-appearing relationship to their patients, and they have probably done the most to promote the concept of treating the whole man. However, if one observes their conditions of practice, it becomes evident that they take many precautions against entering a truly diffuse relationship and against treating anything but a very specific aspect of the man. Psychiatrists usually will not perform a physical examination if a patient is to be treated psychotherapeutically. They have rigid rules against "acting out" in the therapeutic hour—that is, they refuse to grant the patient the leeway of a diffuse relationship. Social contact outside of therapy is sternly discouraged, and, finally, diffuse demands made by the patient are constantly analyzed so that their transference properties are recognized and the doctor-patient relationship remains specific.

With all these precautions, the psychiatrist feels able to interact with the patient in specific ways in order to reach a therapeutic goal. The nurse, however, does not have any such clear-cut safeguards against falling into a *diffuse personal* relationship with the patients.[4]

This does not mean that the nurse must be cold or inhuman with the patients. After all, when people meet on a train or on an airplane and fall into conversation, they are very restricted and uneasy with one another until they get certain facts established. They say "Where are you from?" and "What's your line of business?" before they have a way of evaluating whether they will understand one another's points of view. Similarly, a female patient who has children will feel more able to communicate freely with a nurse if the patient knows that the nurse is married and has children. It goes without saying that the nurse should have sensitivity and understanding about the patients' needs for support and encouragement.

There are two ways in which the nurse keeps the friendly, forthright, supportive relationship from becoming overinvolvement. In the first place, she maintains a focus on action and problem solution, and discussion of interpersonal relationships is in the context of goal-directed activity. When a disturbed patient expresses either affection or hostility toward the nurse, the nurse deals with it primarily in terms of how it will influence the task at hand and not with how it affects their relationship.

The second safeguard is the use of group activities. If the patients spend most of their time in small groups, they will at once come under the norms of behavior of those groups and will also disperse their feelings among a wider group of people. This means that, on the one hand, the tendency to act out will be under social rather than individual control, and, on the other, intense transferences will not have the opportunity to develop.

We realize that there are important disagreements with this point of view. For example, Merton Kahne,[5] in analyzing the effect of the bureaucratic structure of hospitals on patients, says: "I regard the normal functioning of bureaucratic structure as inevitably leading to *impersonal relationships*. [italics ours]." He goes on to say:

> The erotic and aggressive preoccupations of patients coupled with regressive modes of expression exercise a continuous drain on the intellectual and particularly on the emotional resources of personnel. Under such circumstances, where structure makes abdication so easy, detailed rules, regulations, and codes of behavior meticulously organized to keep personal feelings at a minimum provide seductive havens for the avoidance of disagreeable yet perhaps desperately needed experience for patients.

We take issue with this for two reasons. First, as we have said, it is only after years of training and with many safeguards that the psychotherapist undertakes to deal directly with the erotic and aggressive preoccupations of patients, and to ask that nurses and aides do so for the many hours of their working day and for a great deal less money seems somewhat unreasonable. Second, the need to deal directly with these preoccupations arises because they are believed to be the core of the illness. In our view the preoccupations will be mitigated when the ego structure is enhanced through successful performance, both instrumental and interpersonal. The important thing, we feel, is that the successful interpersonal performance can be of many kinds—distant and cool, friendly and warm, or close and expressive; the goal is for the patient to learn to interact appropriately to the occasion.

We know of no studies that undertake to distinguish between those people who can profit by psychotherapy and those who cannot; we might conjecture that certain patients require the sustained interpersonal engagement of psychotherapy, but, in our experience, they might be offered it outside the hospital setting after they are able to cope with social living.

In summary, the psychiatric nurse acting in the therapeutic milieu must be a facilitator and a helper to the patients rather than a therapist—and she must get satisfaction from seeing them achieve greater ego ability. An example will illustrate how subtle this skill must be: A nurse had taken a party of patients for a walk. Upon returning, one patient said: "I'm not coming in." The patient group pointed out that the rules, which they had all made, included being on time for the evening meal. The patient was adamant. The nurse said: "We have all made the rules together, and I am going to stick to them—I'm going in." The group went in, and the recalcitrant patient trailed in behind them. The nurse had acted out her attachment to the common order and her belief in the patient's ability to govern himself in conformity with the rules that he had helped to make.

THE IMMEDIATE THERAPEUTIC ROLE—
AIDE, ATTENDANT, NURSE

The therapeutic agent is the person in contact with the patient. Who this is will depend upon staff ratios. Nurses must be able to plan and administer, but they must also have all the skills of aides and attendants and be able to take their places.

Everything we have said of the nurse holds true for the aide except that he need not have so much ability to administer other people's activities. Ideally, aides should have the same basic attributes as nurses, and then they should be taught how people interact in groups, how norms of behavior are built up, and how "ward cultures" are formed. Probably aides should learn to recognize and experience group pressures and group support in a group-therapy class. They should know enough about work groups to recognize strains when they occur in their own groups and enough about administration to realize why they have to carry out certain procedures in certain ways.

The aide in the therapeutic milieu is a facilitator and guide and not a controller. In many hospitals, furthermore, the aide understands the patients far better than the doctors do. In Weyburn Hospital, for example, during the years when the doctors were all from other parts of the country or from several foreign countries—a common situation in mental hospitals— the male attendants had far more successful ideas for patients' activities than the doctors were capable of inventing. Once the doctors learned to rely on the attendants for the *content* of the daily program, the doctors were able to offer considerable structural support.

In the therapeutic milieu the aide has a much greater voice in the day-to-day program than he has in the old line hospital, but his authority over the patients is not arbitrary. He is the first line of contact for the patient, and he is not only a therapeutic agent in his own right but is also a liaison with the nursing staff. In general, the content of the day-to-day program can be worked out between the aides and the patients. The nurse is a constant source of help and information, but it is the aide upon whom the patient must depend in his everyday interaction.

Because of his role of constant companion and helper to the patient, the aide needs considerable support for himself. This implies more than the support and encouragement he gets from nurses and doctors. In Weyburn Hospital, for example, the attendants were members of both an international union and a nursing organization. In this way the attendants were able to keep their professional standards separate from their grievances and to demand better conditions without feeling "unprofessional." Such institutional supports and affiliations should be encouraged. Aides and attendants are in vulnerable positions in many ways and unless they are confident of backing, they may be overcautious. For example, one older aide with whom we worked bitterly resisted allowing the patients to have watches with them in the hospital until it was discovered that many years before the aide had had to pay for a watch that had been destroyed on the ward. When the aide was assured that the hospital would stand by her, she capitulated.

Not all of these episodes end so happily. Once one of us created a ward disturbance by stopping to speak a few words with an old gentleman being cared for by an aide. The aide misinterpreted the gesture as evidence of his own inability to handle the situation properly and withdrew leaving the old man so confused by the change of situation that he became greatly upset. The aide's fear that his way of caring for the patient was not being confirmed caused the aide to behave abruptly and ambiguously, with disastrous results. These small episodes reveal how much trust must exist between the doctor and the nursing staff in the therapeutic milieu. In this particular case the whole staff became anxious because they had not understood our gesture in stopping to speak to the patient. After the matter had been raised three or four times in ward meetings, we promised the staff that we would never interrupt nurses or aides in the middle of any caretaking act but would bring anything we had doubts about to their attention later. This effectively settled the issue and seemed to give them the security of knowing that we were basically confident of their ability.

Aides should also feel secure in the knowledge that difficulties that cannot be resolved can be referred immediately to a nurse or doctor for corporate solution. In the traditional hospital, attendants often find their own ways of solving problems—many times against the interest of the patients. This need not happen if there is an easily available nurse or doctor to assist the aide when the situation baffles him and if he meets regularly with nurses and patients to discuss problems. In Weyburn Hospital when the attendants on a ward for senile patients asked the attendants from another ward if one of their groups of schizophrenic patients would undertake the task of feeding some of the elderly bedridden patients,* this was arranged in collaboration with the head nurses and the ward doctor, with the ultimate result that the aides had time to get more of their elderly patients out of bed and the schizophrenic patients, in turn, formed friendships with some of the bedridden patients. This episode is a good example of how, when the aide is free to make working decisions and receives adequate support in carrying them out, the ultimate result is that the patients find themselves in a more therapeutic milieu.

In summary, the role of the aide, when clearly specified and adequately supported, adds structure to the patient's en-

---

* These were the same patients who appeared in Chapter 6 being fed with a communal spoon.

vironment, reduces the environment's ambiguity and provides both support and challenge to the patient as he attacks his problems.

THE PATIENTS

The sick person must recognize that he is ill, seek the help of competent persons, and try to follow their instructions if he is to be granted the role of a patient. Mentally ill people sometimes fail to recognize themselves as sick, and their first task is to learn to view themselves as in need of help. This aspect of their role is vitally connected to the issue of freedom. It is an almost unquestioned norm in psychiatry, as it is in society, that freedom for patients is morally good. However, few specific therapeutic reasons have been advanced as to *why* freedom is a good thing. The "open door" was a revelation; we do not question its significance; we are just amazed that it happens at all. The system of informal admissions * recently introduced in English hospitals has the same quality of being accepted almost without question. It is seen as a tour de force but there is little recognition of its significance.

The importance of this development is that the patient, instead of being *committed* to treatment or custody, is placed in the position of *seeking* help from the psychiatrist, who in turn must provide treatment. In this way the patient takes the first step toward *defining himself* as a patient. Thus, a situation similar to another socializing institution, the university, evolves. However, the "students," though adults, have ego capacities by no means up to usual adult standards; yet they cannot be treated as children. The minimum requirements

---

* In England, under the Mental Health Act of 1960, people can now enter mental hospitals without any legal procedure—just as they enter a general hospital.

made of them are similar to those made of university students—
they must participate in the program. Their manner of participating is up to them, but they cannot withdraw from it without being expelled.

Such a model, similar to that of the university, answers
many of the objections that have been made concerning the
mental hospital. Patients can no longer be "mere passive objects
of treatment . . . to be 'cared for,' 'protected,' 'treated,' 're-
spected,' 'handled,' 'controlled' " (Stanton and Schwartz, *The
Mental Hospital*). Neither are they caught at the bottom of a
bureaucratic structure, because they are, in a sense, outside the
structure.

The patient in the free situation finds he must seek help
in learning more effective ways of dealing with everyday life.
Although he is the reason for the existence of the hospital, he
must try hard to get better and to leave it. The hospital staff
must treat the patient as if this were the case: he must never
be relegated to the role of a child through the use of his first
name, through discussion of his problems in front of him, and
through exposure to humiliating procedures that rob him of
the insignia of his adulthood. Until recently, for instance,
almost every hospital routinely removed women's wedding
rings when they were admitted on the theory that valuables
should be safeguarded. In marked contrast are the following
excerpts from the minutes of a ward meeting in Kansas City:

Problem:

Mrs. W. pointed out that a schizophrenic female patient who has
been in the hospital for about three months was evicted from her
rooming house and the social worker had brought her clothing
and all personal belongings over to the hospital in boxes and
bags. Now, we are being held responsible for all this material.
What shall we do about it?

Suggestions from the staff included:

1. Store the material without enumerating it.
2. Enumerate it so that we will not be held responsible for it.

3. Let the patient pack and enumerate the clothing and material
   herself, with the aide to help her if it seems necessary.

Comments:

The doctor suggested that the third solution would be most therapeutic because it would bring the patient back to concrete reality,
and we would be able to observe her reaction to contact with
things that were symbolic of her life outside the hospital. It was
decided to set the patient to this task.

At the next staff meeting it was reported that the experiment had been followed by a marked improvement in this
very ill patient. The solution of this simple problem of storing
goods included such disparate elements as reaffirmation of the
patient's freedom to handle her own belongings, restoration
of part of her adult role, and integration with symbols of her
life outside the hospital, as well as successful problem solution
and, therefore, ego reorganization and perhaps growth.

AUXILIARY ROLES

Finally, there are a number of secondary roles that must
be filled in the hospital. These are the clerical workers, the
maintenance people, and the auxiliary therapists. There is
only one rule regarding them: they should be in the service
of the milieu. Our own work has shown that these categories of
staff usually hold ideas identical to the general public's. One
group of bookkeepers and stenographers whom we studied had
exactly the same stereotyped conceptions of the patients as lay
people who had never been in a hospital. Such staff members
should never make decisions that affect the patients' lives unless they are able to take some part in the therapeutic process.
In Kansas City, when the male patients decided to serve afternoon coffee to the clerks and stenographers, it turned out that
this was the initial visit to the wards for many of them. In
Weyburn Hospital, when the maintenance staff was asked to
confer with the attendants concerning the remodeling of wards,

it seemed to enable them to think in terms of the practical ward problems and this increased their cooperation greatly. Auxiliary personnel should be involved as allies, but decisions about all ward matters should be firmly entrenched in the therapeutic hierarchy.

The volunteer worker can be a godsend or a curse, but she will be the latter if her role is not carefully structured. The nurses and aides can easily find themselves spending valuable time helping the volunteers to help the patient. Volunteers, of course, can do many useful things without interacting with patients—among them clerical tasks. If volunteers are to work directly with patients, it should be under the direction of a staff member who plans their activities, and their appearance on the wards should be fed into the problem-creation, problem-solution sequence of daily life. In general, it is much better that the patients have a party for the volunteers than that the volunteers have one for the patients.

Occupational therapy in the past has been used as a daily routine for the better integrated patients, and it has led to draining the "best" patients from the wards—sometimes into stereotyped activity. Recently, however, some occupational therapists have taken initiative in creating a therapeutic milieu. In some hospitals, O.T. is taken to the wards so as not to break up ward groupings; in others, the O.T. department arranges its program so that groups of patients can work together. And some occupational therapists have been turning to industrial retraining—possibly their biggest future role.

Finally, a word must be said about the relationship of psychotherapy and group therapy to the therapeutic milieu. Group therapy is invaluable to hospitalized patients; it gives them practice in the kind of socio-emotional problem not focused on in instrumental situations. Here the patients learn, or relearn, to keep interpersonal relationships upon an even keel and, with adequate support from their peers, to gain usable insight into their own performance.

Individual therapy is another matter. Although there is no question, as Stanton [6] has pointed out, that milieu therapy helps the psychotherapist, it should be borne in mind that this helpfulness is not necessarily reciprocal outside hospitals where staffing is such that the whole patient population is offered individual therapy. As we have mentioned, in Kansas City we found that the amount of psychotherapy that could be done seemed to accomplish little beyond extending the length of stay of a selected group of patients.[7] The decision to limit hospital treatment to milieu and physical therapies, and to offer psychotherapy upon discharge when it seemed indicated, resulted in a reduced length of stay from about thirty-seven to about twenty-seven days and a more manageable ward situation. It is difficult to keep nurses and aides impressed with the prime importance of their tasks if the doctor regards his therapeutic hours as the only "real" treatment. In this situation nurses and aides either attempt to emulate the doctor, sometimes with disastrous results, or devalue their own contribution. In the large hospital, of course, the doctor simply does not have time for individual therapy except when he is in training, and even then it creates problems. We have found that when residents are being trained in psychotherapy at the same time as milieu therapy, they tend to become overly attached to one or the other and to proselytize for their preferred treatment. This conflict was prevented in Kansas City by dividing the residents' training into milieu therapy while they were attached to the hospital and psychotherapy when they were in out-patient service. The development of short-term, ego-oriented individual therapy such as that suggested by Benson Snyder [8] may in time change this picture entirely. Such therapy, being based essentially on ego theory, may be easier to interpret and practice along with milieu therapy. These are, however, open questions.

Psychologists and social workers have special skills of their own. In some ways they are prepared by their training for the role of team leader, and it may be strategic to use them if they are available in the role specified previously for physicians. In a personal communication to us, Clancey reported asking members of each discipline at Weyburn Hospital to describe the content of their roles. He found extensive overlapping among the roles. In any given hospital, the aspect of the discipline that should be selected for emphasis will depend upon the tasks to be done and the staff available to do them.

We shall leave a discussion of social workers until we consider the community. Although social work is protean and can be used in any setting, its potentiality as the carrier of milieu therapy is greatest in the community.

ROLE INTERRELATIONS

The various roles in a hospital must be linked together, not because this linking results in smoother operation but because, theoretically, a wide range of articulated social roles must be available to patients in order for them to reconstitute ego organizations of adequate complexity for social living. It is our hypothesis that opportunities to take the roles of a variety of other people in clear and unambiguous situations leads to a wider variety of ego sets and better differentiation among these sets. Repeated practice should result in the ability to hierarchize more rapidly and appropriately and to muster ego organizations more effectively. Coordination of a suitable spectrum of activities is achieved through group meetings. The medical direc-tor meets with his doctors to make policy decisions, and the doctors meet with the nurses and ward supervisors. Ward meet-ings must be frequent, and, of course, patients' meetings are part of the daily routine. At all of these policy-creating groupings it is possible to include auxiliary personnel, from the business manager to the head gardener, in order for them to keep abreast of the policies they are expected to carry out—but they should have only an advisory voice in making the policies.*

In all these overlapping systems of group activity there is a cardinal principle: the ways in which those with higher authority treat their subordinates will be reflected in the way in which the latter in turn treat *their* subordinates. Thus the patients who are, for administrative purposes, at the end of an authority chain will receive a true picture of the way in which the different roles are articulated together. When the doctor interacts with his medical director, he is learning how authority roles are conceived in that hospital, and this lesson the doctor will pass on to the nurse. This system of mirrored relationships is sometimes called the "therapeutic atmosphere." Thus, the patient is in a sense learning to relate to people of different authority levels when he interacts with anyone in the hospital.

PROBLEMS TO SOLVE

There are three basic contributions that the role structure of the therapeutic milieu makes to the patient: first, it provides him with a lucid environment; second, it mirrors back to him widely varied aspects of his own nature; and third, through a delegation of a vast amount of task content, it provides him with numerous problems to solve.

The clear structuring of roles in the hospital or the day

---

* There is a multitude of stories of secondary role holders becoming powerful in policy decisions. We have described the hospital steward refusing to issue scissors to the doctors because they had had enough that month already. And we have heard of chief accountants who refused to put in dispensing machines for cigarettes and soft drinks because it made the bookkeeping more complicated, and of personnel directors who ignored medical opinion concerning who should be hired. None of this happens when doctors assume medical responsibility for this type of decision. (See Cumming and Cumming, "The Locus of Power in a Large Mental Hospital.")

center makes it easy for the patient to understand the social environment. Because he sees his own role as a part of this clear structure, the patient knows what is expected of him in the hospital, what tasks he must perform, what support is available to him, and what rewards he may expect.

In this environment, the patient must contract to act in the *whole* patient role; in other words, he is free to act but not free to withdraw. When his abilities in the range of activities open to him—and demanded of him—become clear to the staff, they, and the other patients, can help him to concentrate on the types of roles in which he particularly needs practice. The therapeutic milieu will support the patient in these difficult areas but it will not permit him to select his activities so as to avoid them. For example, a young schizophrenic may require a long program of practice and activity before he can go alone into a store, describe what he wants, and buy it for the ward. It may take him even longer to learn to refuse to buy things he does not want. Both of these things are important instrumental activities; they are part of the fabric of day-to-day competence. In one large hospital where long-stay patients were being rehabilitated, a woman who persistently stole from stores was finally discovered to be doing it because she didn't know *how* to make purchases. For some patients the task of making a bed every day and gathering dirty clothes for laundering can be enormous, but the gain from learning to care for oneself can be equally enormous.

In general, we may say that all personal problems are problems with the content of some role and that some patients will need to learn role elements they have never known, others to differentiate clearly between role elements that have always been unclear to them, and still others to muster the correct role behavior when it is required.

Well-learned role specifications constitute a major part of the self concept. McPartland and Cumming, in "Self-Conception, Social Class, and Mental Health," reported a great loss of references to roles and statuses in the self-concept statements of mentally ill patients. These statements became more like those of well persons as the patients' clinical state improved and, more importantly, remained closely related to their ward behavior. The varied content of activity on the wards can be expected to help to elaborate the role repertoire, the self concept, and the organization of the ego.

To act successfully in an appropriate role is one of the elements of ego identity. The resulting sense of "fit" produces a pleasant ego feeling and thus tends to make such successful performance its own reward. If the hospital or day center is planned so that role learning takes place in a lucid social system, all patients can be expected to improve at least a little.

We shall turn now to the culture of the therapeutic milieu and its influence upon ego restitution.

References

[1] MORGAN MARTIN, "A Practical Treatment Program for a Mental Hospital 'Back' Ward," *American Journal of Psychiatry*, CVI, 10 (1950), 758-760.

[2] IDA ORLANDO, *The Dynamic Nurse-Patient Relationship* (New York: G. P. Putnam's Sons, 1961).

[3] MARK ZBOROWSKI, "Cultural Components in Responses to Pain," in D. Apple (ed.), *Sociological Studies of Health and Sickness* (New York: McGraw-Hill, 1960).

[4] I. L. W. CLANCEY, JOHN CUMMING, and ELAINE CUMMING, "Training Psychiatric Nurses, a Re-evaluation," *Canadian Psychiatric Association Journal*, II, 1 (1957), 26.

[5] MERTON J. KAHNE, "Bureaucratic Structure and Impersonal Experience in Mental Hospitals," *Psychiatry*, XXII, 4 (1959), 370.

[6] ALFRED H. STANTON, "Milieu Therapy and the Development of Insight," *Psychiatry*, XXIV, Supplement to No. 2 (May 1961), 19-29.

[7] ROBERT H. BARNES and THOMAS S. McPARTLAND, "A Redesign of Services in the Urban Mental Hospital" (paper read to Mid-Continent Psychiatric Association Meeting, Little Rock, Arkansas, 1960).

[8] BENSON SNYDER, "Identity Crises in College Students" (paper read to the Annual Meetings of the American Orthopsychiatric Society, 1961).

CHAPTER 8

Culture

In this chapter we shall discuss three related issues: the values and beliefs about "normal" and "abnormal" behavior that the staff and patients, as representatives of the lay public, bring with them to the therapeutic milieu; the professional values and beliefs of the staff; and the way that the culture of the therapeutic milieu is formed and has its influence.

BELIEFS ABOUT MENTAL ILLNESS

We return now to one of the themes of this book—our desire to simultaneously support and control the deviant. In an earlier study [1] we examined the layman's attitudes toward mental illness. Our respondents appeared to believe that mental hospitals are well run, take excellent care of their patients, and have the latest treatments at their disposal. None of this was then true in that place. When they spoke of the mentally ill themselves, these same people were more pessimistic. They described the mentally ill as incurable and unpredictable. This was surprising because most of them said they had known people who had been in mental hospitals and were now well. To understand this paradox we need two more facts: First, the relatives of ex-mentally ill patients very commonly describe them as "not like the rest of them in there—not really insane—just nervous." Second, lay people are extremely reluctant to attach the label "mentally ill" to another person's behavior. Before they will do so, the behavior of a person who has not previously been in a mental hospital must become extremely bizarre.

To sum up this complex of ideas, we might say that the layman has a belief system something like this: most behavior can be thought of as normal and caused by something; however, when a person does become mentally ill he should go to a hospital where everything will be done to cure his incurable illness; if he returns, he was not ill in the first place. By designating the hospitals as good and the mentally ill as in need of permanent isolation, our respondents were able to maintain both their humanitarian attitudes and their solidarity with the nondeviant majority. N. J. Demerath in a much earlier study pointed out that "the conventional values of the 'sane' are reinforced by the hospitalization of the 'insane.' " *

All these findings seem to be manifestations of the conflict central to the social control of deviance that we have discussed before. The dilemmas this conflict creates are resolved in a number of ways, both social-structural and ideological.

A common structural device for neutralizing this conflict is the allocation of its two sides to different role holders. We have discussed how a medical director of a hospital must stand between his staff and society. In the same way, a director of a social agency in carrying out his board's policy acts on the part of society and allocates to his workers the job of being on the

---

* Our formulation, worked out in 1953, was similar to Demerath's 1942 statement.[2] At the time we arrived at ours we had unaccountably not discovered his. The similarity of the formulations appears to have stemmed from common theoretical approaches to the problem.

client's side.* Between these two, a casework supervisor medi-
ates. The position is probably not symmetrical, however, for a
social worker maintains his major loyalty to the normatively
governed society—as both Mills [3] and Davis [4] have pointed out
in analyses of these roles.

The therapeutic stance of "being for the deviant but
against his deviance" is probably essential to success, but it is
difficult because it goes against deeply rooted tendencies to
attribute malignant intention to deviant behavior.[5]

A layman's complex and contradictory ideology appears to
cushion the strains created in society by the need to control
deviance in a humane way. In hospitals and clinics the lay
personnel—aides, cooks, stenographers, bookkeepers, and many
more—all reflect this paradox. In good hospitals ward staffs
believe that their patients are not so ill as those elsewhere, and
in bad hospitals they believe that the patients are incurable and
nothing more can be done for them than they are now doing.
In both cases the ward ideology reconciles beliefs brought from
the greater culture with the observed facts.

An example of this ideological cushioning comes from
Kansas City. A group of thirty-one student nurses were asked
at the end of a twelve-week training period to describe the
difference between their patients and those being admitted to
state hospitals. Although it is hard to compare hospitals, there
was reason to believe that in reality there was little difference.
The nurses, however, had no experience nursing in state hospitals and therefore held laymen's beliefs about them. Most
nurses listed several differences—all incorrect. Of the thirty-one
girls, thirty made one or more of the following distinctions:
Our patients are "acute" whereas those going to the state hospitals are "chronic"; the state hospital patients do not get

---

* The importance of this conflict in the practice of social work was
pointed out to us by Dean Bernard Scher of the School of Social Work
of the University of West Virginia.

better whereas ours do; state hospital patients are sicker and need longer treatment; state hospital patients are insane whereas ours are not. Only three nurses mentioned the one actual difference: the state hospital probably admitted more senile patients.* The following quotation is typical of the group:

> In general, the main purpose of [this hospital] is to socialize and rehabilitate those admitted here. In other words, the goal is to help them help themselves enough to be able to function outside the hospital in a normal, or as near a normal, way as they did pre-admission. However, at State, this is not true. Those patients are not treated with the idea of some day functioning again. They are treated with medication etc. to alleviate their symptoms and maybe try to lessen the severity of the disease. There you found those who are beyond the help of institutions like this one. I am not saying these patients don't get well, as I have no way of knowing, but I do say that when sent to State the "rule of thumb" is to treat without having thoughts of rehabilitation. This is purely opinionated, not based on fact.

Aides in large hospitals have equally effective ways of resolving the conflict. Among the male attendants in Weyburn Hospital there was a surprising unanimity regarding the biological basis of mental illness. A chief male attendant, who later resigned, often expressed the fatalistic belief that schizophrenic patients were born inferior and were beyond help. He looked upon most recoveries as temporary improvements that would soon disappear.† This pessimism was counterbalanced

---

* We are grateful to Miss Elizabeth Helm, Director of Education in the Kansas City Receiving Center, for collecting these data for us.

† It is hard to be quite certain about the connection between professional and lay thinking in this matter. There is a German school that still views schizophrenia much as Kraepelin did—which in turn is much as our attendants did. Americans, on the other hand, tend to designate a group of intractable neurotics as schizophrenics at least partly on the grounds of their resistance to treatment. Concepts such as "pseudo-neurotic schizophrenia" [6] have been medically and ideologically useful in accounting for failure. While professionals call intractable neurotics schizophrenics, ward attendants re-diagnose cured schizophrenics as neurotics.

by a confidence that everything that could be done was being done; the watchword was, "This is the best hospital in the West."

Aides and nurses appear, then, to retain their contradictory attitudes toward mental illness through their explanations of the situations they are in. This fluidity can be helpful to anyone trying to change the attitudes of nurses and aides toward a particular group of patients. We think it important, for example, that a senior aide is able to view the patients more optimistically by asserting that "we don't get the really bad kind that we used to." Even the belief that "you can treat them as long as they don't get to the chronic wards" or that "the drugs make it possible to do things that couldn't be done before" can be regarded as benign fictions playing a part in the transition to more stable positive attitudes. It is up to doctors and nurses to create situations in which aides can help patients get better and thus believe that it is possible. Aides' beliefs about patients in general matter in the same way that lay attitudes matter, and we shall return to this difficult problem in Part III when we discuss the community as milieu.

THE HOSPITAL CULTURE

The helping role is natural and comfortable for a professionally trained nurse, but the content of the therapeutic milieu is often strange and new to her. Therefore, when a doctor fails to communicate his point of view to a nurse and to involve her in the problem-solving process, her starchiness tends to come out.* We have found that almost all nurses will cooperate once they understand the process in which they are expected to take part. Only a minority must be reassigned to tasks less directly

---

* We do not mean to imply that the doctor always has to be the leader. Nurses well trained in milieu therapy can teach a lot of it to residents in the same way that nurses teach interns to do many things.

connected with patients. An occasional nurse must just be endured.

We shall not discuss the basic training of nurses and aides. As we have mentioned before, anyone who works with the mentally ill should have some knowledge of cultural differences, some training in group processes, and some information about the types of mental illness. Aides and attendants should probably all be trained to nurse the physically ill—it increases their repertoire of skills, adds variety to their lives, gives them self-confidence, makes them more useful, and assists them toward a professional image of themselves.

Any doctor who sets out to change the culture of a ward or hospital will have to find a way to feel comfortable in doing it. We and others have recommended beginning by drinking coffee on the wards. Of course, not everyone likes coffee, and not all doctors feel at ease in the informal situation. But as long as a doctor recognizes that the ward culture changes slowly and almost exclusively in interaction, he can approach the nurses in whatever manner seems most natural to him. Furthermore, when a nurse learns that a doctor takes her problems seriously, she will have learned to take her patients' problems seriously. Consider the following excerpt from ward minutes, taken by a nurse, in Kansas City:

The discussion was opened by a nurse stating that she was having a problem with a patient who would not move her feet or help herself, and appeared generally stuporous. A resident had told the ward staff that the patient did this to express her hostility, and not to worry about it. However, the nurses worry when they have to force the patient to do things. The nurse is not sure what the doctor wants. She adds that it upsets the other patients when this stuporous patient is forced to do things, and they think that the nurse is cruel.

Doctor C. suggested that the resident has not fully communicated to the nurse what he wanted done for the patient. The nurse said she wondered if the patient's diabetes had something to do with her behavior. The doctor suggested that the nurse felt uncomfortable using force and being aggressive with a patient who is not openly aggressive to her. All the nurses agreed that this was so.

It was agreed to meet with the resident and explain that the nurses did not think the patient was hostile and did not feel comfortable treating her as if she were.

In this excerpt we see that the nurse starts out by complaining that she cannot understand the doctor but ends by declaring that she does not agree with his diagnosis. The resident in this case is seen as having no faith in the nurse's ability to understand the patient's illness, and the ward doctor is trying to get the resident to talk about the patient with the nurses.

Notice how sensitive this nurse is to the cues the patients are giving her about the treatment of their fellow patient. This suggests patient solidarity and a patient culture. It also suggests that the nurse has a membership in the patients' society and is subject to their social pressures. It is this willingness of the nurse to become vulnerable to the patients' sanctions that gives her a major therapeutic leverage because she has the reciprocal right to influence their behavior with her sanctions.

Here is an excerpt from a research diary note made in a ward staff meeting of another hospital that was just starting a milieu therapy program:

A resident asked what activities should be introduced in the ward. It was decided to have a committee of patients to make ward rules because rule making involves both interaction and decision making—skills that are necessary in the outside world. At the same time, by discussing rules, they are reinforcing their own beliefs about appropriate behavior. A student nurse suggested that completion of the rules would kill the project. Dr. J. suggested that the rules could be reviewed every week.

A patients' newspaper was then suggested, and a member of the Occupational Therapy Department described the history of a previous newspaper that had petered out. It was questioned whether the production of a newspaper was necessarily therapeutic. Some student nurses felt it was a play activity suitable for a scout camp and doubted that it simulated real life. On the other hand, some thought it important for the patients to take the responsibility of finding a typewriter, getting paper, and so on. It was decided that the humdrum parts of the activity were the most therapeutic because in doing them, the patients recover skills.

This meeting shows a break from the tradition of encouraging patients to engage in creative activities.* The therapeutic milieu is utilitarian and does not routinely interest itself in creativity.

THE CULTURE AND NORMS OF THE WARD

Patients arrive in hospitals and clinics declared to be seriously ill by their relatives, friends, and neighbors on the basis of unacceptable behavior. A patient must learn to behave acceptably in order to be considered well again. Ideally a patient should *choose* to behave acceptably, but he has to be *able* to conform before his refusal to do so has any meaning. Conformity, of course, is not the whole answer but only the beginning of social acceptability. Active, motivated, instrumental, or integrative behavior must be regained or learned before conformity has much survival value.

Whether some mental illness is in itself a transition state to be lived through, like grief, is an open question. However, transitional states are probably diagnosable, and a doctor sensitive to the possibility of their existence can arrange to have patients supported in the expression of symptoms related to these states. We are inclined to think that a lot of research is needed to clarify the frequency, kinds, and variations of transition states.

We have stated before that the milieu must provide the patients with culturally relevant problems. In many chronic

---

* Any evidence of creativity would, of course, be warmly welcomed, but it is evident that patients, like the rest of us, are infrequently creative. At Ville Evrard, in Paris, where great emphasis is laid on "creativity," a staff member showed us with sorrow how one patient had become less creative and more banal as his psychosis had come into remission.

hospitals the separation of the sexes is a violation of the normal pattern of living in the larger society. Fortunately, since the war when a shortage of men resulted in women aides nursing mentally ill men, there has been a tendency toward a more normally organized life in large hospitals. However, there is still considerable distance to go: the inflammatory influence of the opposite sex upon psychotics is one of the great myths of all times, but it is still believed by many people.

By contrast, in smaller hospitals there is sometimes a tendency to expect patients to show the same sophisticated attitudes toward sex as the doctors do.* The following excerpt from a research diary illustrates this point:

A schizophrenic female had been home for a week-end and told her sister that she had lost her virginity in the hospital. It was found upon investigation, that the patient and her boyfriend had been seen necking by the dietitian and had been given a sort of tacit approval. The nurses knew that they had been together quite a bit. The resident had handled the situation by telling the patients that necking was against the hospital rules. It was agreed in staff discussion that adultery in the hospital is like suicide, a disapproved act that sometimes occurs in the outside world. The incidence of both suicide and adultery can be cut down by strict supervision. When doors are opened and some of the controls released, the suicide rate rises to that of the outside society † and perhaps the adultery rate too, although this seems less likely. When we suddenly free the patient's environment, we must establish new social controls to take the place of the ones we have removed.

---

* Some generally accepted psychiatric ideas are quite deviant by working-class standards. Rapaport has criticized Jones' therapeutic community on the grounds that it became such a separate, deviant subculture that the patients who made the best adjustment in the hospital were least able to adjust to the standards of the outside community.

† This entry indicates that the authors themselves have been erroneously caught up in the belief system. Sainsbury [7] has recently shown that suicide rates in mental hospitals in Great Britain remained constant in the period 1930-1950, when there was either no treatment or only physical treatment. However, between 1950 and 1960, with the introduction of the open hospital and greater patient freedom, the suicide rate dropped.

An interesting cultural problem concerns the relationship between Negro and white patients. In the Kansas City hospital there were about the same number of Negro as white patients. When the patients went in groups to restaurants, they met difficulty in being served as a racially mixed group. They became very cohesive as a result and very resourceful about getting service at places that normally excluded Negroes. Yet when these same patients planned an alumni club, it was in terms of two racially segregated groups that would meet separately.* The staff were in conflict, but they decided that the patients had to be allowed to solve their cultural problems in terms of their own cultural standards. If patients achieve the strength to challenge beliefs that the doctors think are retrograde, this is a gratuitous cause for rejoicing. A doctor himself need never behave as if he approves of segregation if he does not—on the contrary, he can be honest about his position. But his job is to help people to be strong enough to live their own lives; if major cultural values appear to be inimical to health, the doctor can join reform organizations, not make the patient his agent. This is easier said than done, however: it is very hard to decide in practice where freeing the patient from paralyzing rigidity leaves off and teaching him "liberal" values takes over. Nevertheless, if approached honestly, culture conflict is an area offering great opportunities for ego growth.

Aggression and violence present an important value problem to patients. Middle-class staff members tend to underestimate the power of patient groups to handle their own psychotic members when they become aggressive. Even a compulsive talker—the bane of staff meetings—can usually be handled by patient groups because the solidarity among the patients as well as the problem of "getting along together"

---

* Constance Osgood in a personal communication to the authors.

allows them to be frank in expressing disapproval of unacceptable behavior.

Matters that do not have a value problem attached to them can still make a great difference to a ward. For example, in a study of a general hospital ward, Peter New [8] found that nurses who complained that administrative routines took too much time from bedside nursing spent the same proportion of time administering when the staff was doubled. Apparently, in the absence of a plan for a new routine, the old norms about the allocation of time still held.

Doctors are less susceptible to any particular norm because they interact with a wider variety of groups and have the job of integrating the values and norms of ward working groups with the policy of the hospital. In doing this doctors are exercising an important form of leadership. Nurses, aides, and patients often work under stressful conditions and need a lot of support from doctors, who are not so bound to the concrete situation. A doctor, therefore, must look upon attendance at ward meetings and at medical staff meetings as a primary call on his time —especially when he is tempted to skip them because the meetings are difficult and he cannot decide what to do next.

Finally, a doctor seems to have to endure ambiguity at the same time that he is clarifying the situation for staff and patient. If he keeps a variety of ideas in his own head, while he waits for problems to be voiced, he can move in to support and enhance practical suggestions that are close to the lives of his patients and, therefore, have meaning.

We have found that some ward staffs will ask a doctor for formal lectures. First, they listen avidly, then their interest lags—sometimes before the doctor's has done so. We have found, for reasons that we do not really understand, that ward staffs tend to alternate acute interest in the theory behind their jobs with commitment to intense task activity. If these cycles are used as they occur, they can give a flexible, functional tone to the relationship between doctor and staff. This, in turn, will be reflected in the staff's relationship with patients.

We have discussed the hospital, but whenever people work together, culture forms. In a clinic, for example, the receptionist communicates the culture to the patient. The clinic that sets its patients the task of filling out a complex application form while sitting in a dark corner of a waiting room is communicating quite clearly that it values the presence of only better-integrated patients. Perhaps when a clinic policy includes treating only the well-motivated patient, it must also include only those with strong enough egos to pass the "motivation tests."

A receptionist who asks personal questions in a loud voice can put a patient under intolerable stress. Clinic physicians can avoid this kind of thing if they have conferences concerning intake procedures and include all staff members in them.

CULTURE, NORMS, AND EGO GROWTH

Culture is intimately related to ego restitution. In the first place, cultural familiarity prevents diffusion feeling and alienation, and, conversely, an understanding of the culture prevents ambiguity and further ego insult by helping the patient to maintain differentiation.

The second important contribution of a well-developed ward culture is the opportunity for a patient to learn roles in a context that resembles in some ways the context in which he will be acting in the future. In this way, the fit between the individual and the situation—that is, ego identity—will be developed in a manner that will allow it to be projected forward into life outside the hospital. A patient may accordingly develop confidence in his ability to maintain ego organization.

An ego-damaged patient is in a sense deculturated; the goal is to bring him back into sufficient relationship with social life to allow him to work out his own unique compromises between individuality and conformity. The restoration of acceptable behavior is particularly important for a mentally ill patient because it helps restore to him the label "normal" that leads to social acceptability. This, in turn, should allow a patient to attempt more difficult tasks and to develop stronger, more complex, and more clearly differentiated ego organizations and a greater ego ability.

In the next chapter we shall conclude our discussion of the structural aspects of the milieu by considering the problem of communicating with severely ill patients.

References

[1] ELAINE CUMMING and JOHN CUMMING, *Closed Ranks* (Cambridge, Mass.: Harvard University Press, 1957).

[2] N. J. DEMERATH, "Social Solidarity and the Mental Hospital," *Social Forces*, XXI, 1 (October 1942), 67.

[3] C. W. MILLS, "The Professional Ideology of Social Pathologists," *American Journal of Sociology*, XLIX, 2 (1943), 165.

[4] KINGSLEY DAVIS, "Mental Hygiene and the Class Structure," *Psychiatry*, 1 (1938), 55.

[5] FRITZ HEIDER, *The Psychology of Interpersonal Relations* (New York: John Wiley & Sons, 1958).

[6] PAUL HOCH and PHILLIP POLATIN, "Pseudoneurotic Forms of Schizophrenia," *Psychiatric Quarterly*, 23 (1949), 248.

[7] PETER SAINSBURY, "Suicide in Old Age," *Proceedings of the Royal Society of Medicine*, LIV, 4 (April 1961), 266.

[8] PETER K. NEW, GLADYS NITE, and JOSEPHINE M. CALLAHAN, *Nursing Service and Patient Care, A Staffing Experiment* (Kansas City, Mo.: Community Studies, 1959).

CHAPTER 9

Communication

Communication is at once an end in itself and a means to an end. As an *end* in itself it seems to be intrinsically and ubiquitously attractive. As Suzanne Langer [1] has pointed out, humans are able to use the production of symbols artistically and playfully in order to express their essential humanity. But it is not this ability that we are concerned with here; before a patient with serious ego damage can play and create, his ability to work and to relate in everyday situations must be reinstated.

As a *means* to an end, communication pervades all aspects of life. We have already mentioned that in the therapeutic community adequate communication systems are necessary for proper role integration, for the exercise of legitimate authority, and for the creation and transmission of culture. In this chapter, we shall discuss the microscopic process of interpersonal communication rather than the institutionalization of communication channels.

LAYERS OF COMMUNICATION

Gregory Bateson [2] used a logician's term—"metacommunication"—to describe the fact that around every cognitive mes-

sage there lies a wrapping of communications about the communication. Bateson's original insight, he declares, came to
him in a zoo while he was watching monkeys playing at fight-
ing, as children do. He had seen the monkeys both fight and
play and he could not tell the difference between the individual
gestures of an angry monkey and a playful one; both looked
equally aggressive. He concluded that the monkeys in some
way were able to get across to one another the message, "this
is play," so that the gestures could be properly interpreted. This
raises a question, however: How is it done?

Talcott Parsons [3] in a discussion of symbolic behavior suggests a solution when he points out that the production of
symbols is normatively governed.

> . . . When two boys are "roughhousing" we would say that a
> blow beyond a certain level of intensity is established as an "aggres-
> sive act" whereas short of this it may be friendly "fooling around."
> The boy who exceeds the limit may, if he hits his partner too hard,
> get him "mad" even if he did not intend to . . . because he has
> violated the established convention of the expressive meaning of
> an act.

In short, this kind of communication requires some qualitative
symbolic message, or metacommunication, that says in the
first place, "this is play," and then requires a normatively established quantitative convention that thereafter confines the
interaction to play.

Metacommunications do more than signal the affective
meaning of actions, however. They also pinpoint the meaning
of the cognitive message in other ways. Some metacommunications give information about the connotations that should be
put upon certain words. For example, the word "incestuous"
has denotations of illicit sexual relations, but if a speaker says,
"That sounds downright incestuous to me," it may be his tone
or his expression or gesture or even the position of the word in
the sentence that determines whether this phrase means literally

incestuous, or something like "unwholesomely closely tied to one another"—a dramatically different meaning. The word has become almost, but not quite, a metaphor. The exact point between metaphorical and literal truth is indicated by the tone of voice, facial expression, muscle tension, phrasing, and so on of the speaker. It seems possible that the connotations of key words must all be established before sustained communications can take place.

In one way the metacommunicative aspects of an interchange seem more covert than the cognitive aspects. That is, they do not yield so readily to verification. For example, one cannot turn to a third person and say, "You heard *how* he said that," the way one can say, "You heard *what* he said." Nevertheless, metacommunications are persistent necessary accompaniments to communication, and without them the meaning of the cognitive messages themselves are often obscure—as anyone who has tried to make sense of a tape-recorded transcript of a meeting can attest. In this sense they are an overt and intrinsic part of any message.

We can call the cognitive communication,* and the metacommunications that make its meaning more precise, the *manifest message*. However, along with many messages go accompanying latent communications that are not the main burden of the message nor necessarily related to it.† These latent parallel communications may be concerned with the relative status of those giving and receiving the messages. For

---

* One of the arguments against treating patients in bureaucratic structures is concerned with communication and goes something like this: Folk language has phonemes isomorphic with the affects appropriate to them. Depersonalized languages do not. In bureaucracies, technical, impersonal language robs a patient of the opportunity to communicate in language that allows him to reintegrate meaning and affect easily because of the isomorphism. Ironically, this is an argument for the use of less highly trained aides rather than nurses, etc.

† These are obviously only relatively latent; if they were fully latent, they could not be received.

example, when a group of parents discussing their children are joined by a newcomer, the conversation changes quality when it is discovered that he is a bachelor.* This revelation allows the bachelor's listeners to evaluate his opinions in a different light than they would if he were a parent and perhaps even to perceive his opinions as having a different meaning. Like metacommunications assigning meaning to key concepts, these latent messages need be given only at the beginning of a conversation. If the participants know one another well and have previously discussed the topic, the latent messages about cognitive and instrumental matters can be omitted altogether. This makes communication easy and efficient, but it can make outsiders very uncomfortable.

In all successful communication, when the frame of reference is changed the change is signaled with such warnings as, "You know, I was just thinking . . ." or, "By the way. . . ." Such phrases say only that a change is coming.

A second type of latent communication is concerned with what each of the people in an interaction is expecting. In normal interaction, the actions of one person are constantly influenced by the expectation of the other. Even when an action deliberately violates an expectation, as it does in jokes and repartee, these violations are themselves normatively governed. Early in childhood the desire to do what is going to be rewarded as appropriate is learned, and this is the keystone of society. However, people do not learn what is valued and then act on their knowledge; in all interaction there are ongoing rewards and sanctions: smiles, frowns, sighs, all telling

---

* There are interesting cross-national differences in this type of communication. The British almost always give an overt role definition when they introduce people: "This is Mr. so-and-so; he is in publishing," whereas Americans feel that such identifications are somehow "undemocratic." They are much more likely to say, "This is my friend Joe Smith," or perhaps even just "Joe." As a result, more skill in undercurrent communication about status is needed.

us that we are being understood, that the relationship is being overextended, that the subject is appropriate, that this is the wrong place for this kind of talk, that this is just what we have been longing to hear, and countless other guides. This kind of latent communication allows a mother, when guests are present, to tell a child to go to bed in such a way as to communicate either that she expects the child to reappear again or that she will trounce him if he does. Sometimes the guests can decode these latent messages because all parents give them, and sometimes the child cannot because he has had too little practice; but in the end, if all goes well, the child will be able not only to understand such private communications but also to give them.

Such a complex process as communication and its penumbra of metacommunication and latent messages would take the total attention if its normative quality were not firmly established and its more mechanical aspects committed to reflex—or near reflex—activity, so that even the unexpected can be met in an expected way. Mistakes happen, sometimes embarrassing mistakes, but they are quickly cleared up. However, in the ego-damaged patient, in ways that we do not yet fully understand, the ability to give and receive communication becomes impaired. In order to consider the problems that the ego-damaged patient faces, we shall briefly discuss some of the confusions that occur in communication.

PROBLEMS IN EVERYDAY COMMUNICATIONS

Anxiety can easily be aroused by poor communication. If we stay for long among people who are talking in terms we do not understand, we soon ask ourselves the anxious question, "Are they crazy, or am I?" Even inconsequential miscommunications take more of the attention than they deserve. For example, we once overheard a colleague say, "They're beside the pile of ice-cubes on my desk." This phrase kept jumping to the center of consciousness until we realized that he was saying "pile of I.Q.'s." But these are trifling problems because they are unique and passing. When distorted or ambiguous communication becomes established as a pattern, it is more serious, as Bateson and his co-workers have inferred from their extensive inquiries into the communication patterns of families of schizophrenics. However, little is known about the range of communicative behavior, and it is hard to be sure of what is normal. We still do not know that the patterns Bateson found are related to the disease in any causal way.

Bateson originally distinguished what he called the "double bind." This is the situation that results when the metacommunicative message contradicts the cognitive message.* An example is the response of a busy mother when her child has fallen and, although unhurt, is crying for comfort. She stops what she is doing and says with great irritation, "Oh, come here then." The mother's words tell her child that he may come for the comfort he so badly wants, but her tone tells him to stay away because she is in no mood to give the comfort that she recognizes it is her duty to give. Presumably, every child learns to select which of two such contradictory messages to respond to and thus exercises his ability to choose between alternatives—that is, to hierarchize his ego sets. Bateson argues, however, that this pattern, if repeated, is schizophrenogenic,† and it is reasonable, in terms of our theory, to suppose that a child surrounded by a number of people who related to him in this way might develop a chronic inability to judge which of the two sides of a communication to respond to. This in turn would lead to an impaired ability, under less binding circumstances, to select ap-

---

* In double binds there is often no right response. One solution may be to maintain ambiguity. This leads to inaction, no learning, and also anxiety since unresponsiveness may also be sanctioned.

† For a full explanation of the conditions basic to the double bind, the reader is urged to consult Bateson's referenced works.

propriate ego sets in assigning relative importance to mixed messages. And this in turn might lead to poor differentiation among ego sets and therefore to an inadequate ego structure.

It should be remarked in passing that the bind seems to be a universal form of social sanction and is especially useful when no open expression of anger is feasible. If we wait half an hour on a corner for a friend who is late, he does not blame us if we ask pleasantly, "What's the matter, were you in a bar?" If he bridles and tries to break the bind by saying, "No, I was held up by business," we can hammer it in by saying, "Can't you take a joke?"

Bateson and his co-workers [4] have described another communication pattern characteristic of the families of schizophrenics: the tendency to make a positive statement weakened by a modifier or a contradiction. When two people both do this, a characteristic resonance sets up. One may say, "Let's go to the 9 o'clock movie; [pause] perhaps we should stay home." The other may reply, "Yes, let's stay home; [pause] the 7 o'clock movie would be better." Bateson and his co-workers have observed that this type of communication goes along with unstable alliances and shifting power groupings. In a schizophrenic's family nobody knows who is going to be siding with whom from one moment to the next.

When we examine this procedure in terms of our theory, we see a curious thing. It is as if each member of the communicating team was unable to clarify and hierarchize his ego sets sufficiently to select one and make a decision. This in turn is mirrored in the partner. The upshot is that each is trying to play his own role and the role of the other simultaneously; neither can go through the normal process of taking the role of the other in order to understand his communication and then act out his own role in the light of that communication; that is, there is no clear role demarcation. This blurring of roles could lead to identity confusion, ego boundary disorders, poor differentiation, and failure to hierarchize. This malfunction can be compounded if neither of the partners has firm *external* role anchorages such as are supplied by a strong occupational identity that can give him a basis for decision.

It is probable that isolated episodes of this type of interaction occur in everyday life. When they do, the feeling of diffusion that accompanies them probably acts as a stress, mobilizes resources, and leads to a swift resolution.

It is possible to speculate that when the ego is poorly differentiated and the hierarchizing of sets is difficult, the ability to act may depend upon the role partner. A well-integrated person may force his indecisive role partner to assume a submissive role. Over long periods of interaction, the submissive partner's ego may strengthen and differentiate within the limits of the constricted role activity associated with being submissive.

However, if a person with only moderately well-differentiated and organized ego sets interacted with another over a period of time, he might *through his equivocal communication alone* induce in the other his own condition. Certainly children taking the role of such a parent could reasonably be expected to lack ability to hierarchize ego sets. Speculating further, our theory would suggest that Bateson and his co-workers in describing these families have identified an ego-undermining and possibly schizophrenogenic process. It would be interesting to know such things as whether the reason the parents themselves are not schizophrenic is because they are able to act effectively in some external role, and what happens to children in families in which only one parent is afflicted with this debility.

In general, the intact ego appears able to make extremely subtle interpretations of extremely complex communication. The ego-damaged person, however, seems to have great difficulty in understanding what is being addressed to him. At present we do not know how much of his confusion is caused by an inability to understand the cognitive message, how much is a disorder of the receiving apparatus, and how much is an inability to understand the relationship among the various messages. We do know that in a general way anxious people, neurotic people, and psychotics have difficulties of various kinds both in sending and receiving communications. There has been much study of the most disordered psychotic communication, but possibly because in the psychotherapeutic relationship the flow of conversation is from patient to doctor, little attention has been paid to the fact that a psychotic patient finds it as hard to receive messages intelligibly as he does to put them out. Furthermore, psychotherapeutic interests have been upon content and meaning, and, with some exceptions, attention has been directed away from the communication process itself.

COMMUNICATING WITH PATIENTS

Patients vary in their ability to communicate. Many can be assumed to be communicating well enough so that no special precautions need be taken. New patients, of course, have the same difficulty in relating to staff members that strangers usually have in getting into conversations with each other, and for this reason staff members must take most of the initiative for establishing the patient's status—and their own—and for making explicit any language peculiar to the hospital culture. That is, the messages that can be latent after the patient is used to the hospital will have to be made manifest when he is a newcomer.

Some psychotics have marked disorders of cognitive and affective communication and are totally unable to sort out latent messages, or if they can understand them, they cannot place them in context. Moreover, as we have reported elsewhere (in "Affective Symbolism, Social Norms, and Mental Illness"), most ward staff members are less troubled by bizarre cognitive distortions than they are by quantitative distortions of affective symbols and disordered metacommunications in general. We found that patients who were mute or overly demanding were far more troublesome to unsophisticated staffs than patients who were deluded and hallucinated. The latter seemed blameless because they were crazy; the former appeared to know what was appropriate to say but through stubbornness or ill will chose to say too little or too much.

Because of the anxiety and, probably, diffusion feelings that patients arouse in others, it is imperative to equip staff members with techniques for relating to a patient so that they will not communicate their dismay and further alienate the patient.

Ward aides and attendants are put at a disadvantage in some hospitals by entering a culture that has traditionally emphasized a "professional" relationship with patients that was essentially formal and distant. A good nurse can find common personal ground with a patient without becoming overinvolved. In a sense, all communication involves giving a little of the self into the interaction and getting something of the other in return. If the output is all on one side, the process breaks down. It is possible to teach this concept of communication with the example of two strangers striking up a conversation on a train.* If one opens with, "Going far?" the other has several alternatives. He can answer with a bare, "Yes." Everyone recognizes this as meaning, "I don't wish to pursue this subject any further." If, however, he says, "Yes, I'm going to New York City," it leaves the responsibility of continuing to the initiator but does not close the discussion. Finally, if he says, "I'm going to New

---

* This sequence can be used as a role-playing exercise for training aides. They can play out several different sequences and analyze the feeling tone that develops in each. The observers seem to learn by empathy as much as the participants do. The process is discussed in a work by John Cumming.[5]

York; where are you going?" he is clearly willing to proceed. The first answer is discouraging because it gives nothing of the self; the second offers something of the self; and the third both offers information about the self and asks for information from the other, thus setting the stage for the cycle of the give and take of communication to begin again.

It is obvious that different types of ego damage lead to different communication difficulties. Neurotic patients with their inappropriate use of sets may need no particular care, but psychotics with disorganized or weak egos must at first be given especially lucid messages.

Schizophrenics, with their obvious confusion, are perhaps the prototype of the communication-deficient patient. Not only do they have trouble sending messages about their own affective states—even supposing that they can send adequate cognitive ones—but they also have considerable trouble receiving them. They appear to miss latent messages and metacommunications, so that they are often doubtful about *why* certain messages have been directed to them even though they have perceived the cognitive meaning. For this reason schizophrenics frequently misinterpret what is said to them. Nurses and aides should probably learn to ask the newly admitted schizophrenic if he has understood them and to translate nonverbal communications into verbal ones. Instead of assuming that a patient can follow their facial expressions, decode their tone of voice, and so on, staff members can at first tell a patient in words what their reactions are. It makes the communication process clumsy to have to say, "I'm pleased," "I'm impatient," "I'm a little tired," and so on when a gesture would suffice, but it seems to work. In the most acute phases, schizophrenics appear to suffer from complete inability to take the role of the other, to understand what is expected of them, to relate separate items of communication together, and even to receive cognitive messages.

In this stage of ego dedifferentiation and disorganization, clear, well-organized orienting communications may be the most effective therapeutic tool.

Communication is less dramatically obvious a problem with a patient being cared for in a community facility. However, symbol production, metacommunications, and latent messages are all normatively governed processes, and the norms vary both by culture and by class. Because of this, messages that seem normal in the neighborhood seem disordered and alien in the clinic. Cultural expectations of clinic staff are, after all, vastly different from those of patients. Several authors [6] have suggested that people in the bottom half of the class structure are unacceptable for psychotherapy—as well as being less likely to be treated once they get into a hospital. It seems probable that a complicated failure of communication causes this. Less well-educated members of society do not seem to manipulate verbal symbols so skillfully as the better educated, nor have they access to as many of them.* Many psychiatrists, however, use words as their main therapeutic tool. Furthermore, the norms governing their use vary by culture and class. Mark Zborowski (in "Cultural Components in Responses to Pain") has shown that culturally appropriate communication of physical suffering varies widely among Americans of Yankee, Jewish, and Italian origins. These responses, entirely "normal" within each of the three groups, are evaluated by middle-class doctors as ranging from appropriate to cowardly in terms of their own middle-class values.

---

* Education is a powerful influence on satisfaction with life. Gerald Gurin and his co-authors [7] say that highly educated people tend to have at the same time a greater sense of well-being and a greater sense of inadequacy than the less well educated. These authors point "to education as broadening one's perspective and raising one's aspiration level—which leads to both an increased realization of problems and unfulfilled expectations, and a greater awareness of life satisfactions." Such people might be more likely to seek psychotherapy. Our society does not readily accept the idea that pain is inevitable.

PROBLEM SOLUTION AND EGO RESTITUTION

Communication appears to be closely tied to the maintenance of ego integrity. Just as the communication itself is dependent upon a coherent organization of symbols, so, in a parallel way, are set differentiation and ego organization—and hence self concept and identity—dependent upon reinforcement in consistent relationships with others. In interaction we are able to set forth our perceptions of ourselves and our roles as well as our expectations of others and our cognizance of them. If the responses we get indicate an acceptance of this aspect of our messages, our self concept and identity are reinforced. Conversely, most messages directed toward us carry "to-whom" labels that tell us our roles, what is expected of us, and, indeed, something about our very nature. Our acceptance of these estimates or our rejection or modification of them are all maneuvers that result in retention and verification of our ego identity and self concept, even though this may not be their primary intent.

In other words, an important part of our assumptive state —our idea of the nature of the world—is our concept of all aspects of ourselves. For most people, this seems curiously fragile, tending to become vague or disordered if not constantly reinforced. Thus the recurring life problem—"Who am I?"— seems to have to be solved and solved again in everyday life. There is, of course, a core of self concept that can be held situation free and projected forward or backward in time. Nevertheless, every time the situation changes, some new answer must be available because identity is always related to situation, although the relationship may be tenuous for considerable periods of time. Fortunately, in everyday life the question can be put, and satisfactorily answered, hundreds of times each day. Perhaps the disorganization felt in loneliness, in isolation, or even during hospitalization for physical illnesses arises partly from the difficulty of getting clear and unambiguous confirmations of our perpetual questioning of our identity.

Communication helps to resolve the problem "Who am I?" and, in doing so, it resolves the complementary problem "What is the nature of the world?" All the messages that locate an individual in social and psychological space also locate those with whom he interacts. If an individual is vague about the situation, he experiences unpleasant ego feeling, and he attempts to remove this by a selection of ego sets appropriate for clarifying the situation; a resolution of the question of why the situation is ambiguous brings, simultaneously, a confirmation of the appropriateness of the choice of sets and, hence, identity. Thus, although communication is only a means to an end—except in the pure expressivity of art and play—it is a means to the most vital of ends—our knowledge of ourselves and of the world.

In summary, whether communication problems are the cause or the result of pathology is still unproven. However, we do know that unambiguous communication seems to help schizophrenics to return to normative control. Furthermore, our theory suggests that ambiguous communications, communications with double meanings, and communications which betray poor role-taking ability would invoke in an already ego-damaged patient further blurring of identity, further dedifferentiation of sets, and further ego disorganization. For these reasons, simple, clear communication appears indicated for a newly hospitalized psychotic patient. Methods of communication can gradually become more complex until the patient is able to carry on normal interaction with the staff and those outside. However, staff members can be equipped with specific skills for communicating with patients so that distortions do not confuse the patients and render staff members unable to get in effective therapeutic contact with them.

References

¹ SUZANNE LANGER, *Philosophy in a New Key* (Cambridge, Mass.: Harvard University Press, 1942).

² GREGORY BATESON, "A Theory of Play and Fantasy," *Psychiatric Research Reports,* No. 2, American Psychiatric Association (December 1955).

³ TALCOTT PARSONS, "The Theory of Symbolism in Relation to Action," in Talcott Parsons, Robert F. Bales, and Edward A. Shils (eds.) *Working Papers in the Theory of Action* (Glencoe, Ill.: Free Press, 1953), 39.

⁴ GREGORY BATESON, D. D. JACKSON, J. HALEY, and J. WEAKLAND, "Toward a Theory of Schizophrenia," *Behavioral Science,* 1 (1956), 251.

⁵ JOHN CUMMING, "Communication: An Approach to Chronic Schizophrenia," in Lawrence Appleby, Jordan M. Scher, and John Cumming (eds.) *Chronic Schizophrenia* (Glencoe, Ill.: Free Press, 1960).

⁶ JEROME K. MYERS and BERTRAM H. ROBERTS, *Family and Class Dynamics in Mental Illness* (New York: John Wiley & Sons, 1959).

⁷ GERALD GURIN, JOSEPH VEROFF, and SHEILA FELD, *Americans View their Mental Health* (New York: Basic Books, 1960), p. 211; see also S. BUDNER, H. ESECOVER, S. MALITZ, and B. WILKENS, "The Relationship between Staff Values and Choice of Treatment" (paper read to the Downstate Psychiatric Meetings of the New York Department of Mental Hygiene, April 1961).

197

PART III

EGO IN MILIEU

Introduction to Part III

In Part II we discussed aspects of the structure of the therapeutic milieu as if it were in a vacuum and often in ideal terms. In this Part, we shall discuss specific problems and processes. In Chapter 10 we shall outline some of the problems associated with the treatment of the acutely ill patient and try to evoke an image of the therapeutic milieu in operation. In Chapter 11 we shall discuss work programs as they are related to problems of chronicity and rehabilitation. In Chapter 12 we shall turn our attention to the distribution in the community of people with serious ego damage and discuss some of the problems of supporting and controlling them in their natural environments. We shall be especially interested in the problem of providing a structured milieu outside a hospital setting. We shall briefly discuss the family and suggest some manipulations that can make it a more benign environment for its ego-damaged members. We shall suggest the importance of the school and the job as pervasive influential milieus in which everyone at some time finds himself. We shall mention some areas in which we think research is needed—although we do not subscribe to the view that practice is *necessarily* better because research is going on.

To us, Chapter 12 is as important as it is incomplete because, although the large hospitals are doing the most efficient job in their history, they are, nevertheless, increasingly unpopular.* At the same time, although the efficacy of the individual therapies is being seriously questioned for the first time, they remain the backbone of psychiatric training programs.

One of the problems that we have implicitly raised in this book, especially in this Part, is how to deploy the resources of the healing and helping arts so that those who need treatment will be able to get it under conditions commensurate with that human dignity with which every person is expected to be equally credited.

In Chapter 13 we shall try to gather up some loose ends and point out some open areas in the theory and in the practices based on this theory. We shall discuss briefly the problems to be anticipated in evaluating milieu programs. We shall suggest the underlying model of man that our scheme appears to rest on, and we shall indicate the ethical posture that we think the milieu therapist can strike. Finally, we shall propose a tentative new place for the theory in the medical nexus.

---

* There is some reason to believe that their unpopularity with psychiatric personnel is not reflected in public sentiment; on the contrary, people are entering them on a voluntary basis in increasing numbers.

CHAPTER 10

Treatment of Acute Ego Damage

Our purpose in this chapter is to give some idea of the day-to-day process of milieu therapy, to discuss some of the major issues that arise in the treatment of the acutely ill patient, and to suggest in terms of our theory why certain techniques are particularly successful.

We shall start with the admission of a patient to a hospital or day center, partly because this is the beginning of the treatment process, but also because it is where the hospital meets the community. In Part II, in order to highlight some of its defining characteristics, we described the therapeutic milieu as if it existed in a vacuum. Now we shall try to show how the milieu is articulated with the community while we are describ-ing the therapeutic process. As Querido [1] says: ". . . in the last analysis the cure or the adaptation of the mentally disturbed can only be accomplished in society and . . . a successful stay in society is the only real test of any therapeutic endeavor."

LEAVING THE COMMUNITY

Ideally, the admission of patients to a hospital should start in the community itself; in both Britain and Holland this has been found feasible. In Mapperley Hospital in Nottingham, England, Duncan Macmillan uses this principle for all admissions.* In 1960 we accepted his invitation to accompany him and a social worker on a "domiciliary visitation" for the purpose of assessing a patient's need for hospitalization. The social worker had previously seen the patient on the recommendation of a general practitioner, and she explained the background of the problem to us in the car. We found the patient, an old nearly deaf man, living alone with his wife.

Our diary notes read:

Dr. Macmillan asked the wife to tell him the trouble. She said that her husband was 82 and that he had been fine until recently when he had fallen and injured his back; then, while convalescing, he had become confused and has since been getting worse. "He needs to be watched all the time," she said. "I haven't had my clothes off for a week except for one night when my daughter-in-law came and sat with him. . . . He wandered out of the house last week and got his head caught in the neighbor's door and then cried out and scared them." Then she told us that he had taken to following the clock face around and reciting the numbers out loud for minutes on end. Her voice trembled; she said it was very difficult to listen to him go on and on, and she no longer dared to leave him alone. She wept a little.

Macmillan asked a few more questions about the onset of the confusion, looked into the old man's mouth, and commented that his teeth were in terrible condition. (He had concluded that the rather sudden onset of the illness, the patient's confusion, and his less than optimal physical condition all suggested that this might be a toxic reaction.) After he had finished the assessment, Macmillan said firmly and cheerfully to the wife, "He must come to the hospital for three or four weeks." Before she could answer he said, "It's not because you haven't been to bed, you know; it's because he's ill and we must build him up and fix his teeth and try to make him as well as he was before he fell." Then he turned to the old man and shouted to him that he must go to the hospital, but the old man replied quickly, "Oh no, I shouldn't like that."—But then he hesitated

---

* For a detailed description of his whole scheme of operation see the work of Macmillan.[2]

and said softly, "I'll do anything to save my wife trouble; I'd rather do anything than to cause her trouble."

Dr. Macmillan asked the wife to explain to her husband that he would be able to come home again, and she shouted to him that he was only to go for a week or two, but Macmillan corrected her and shouted, "You must come into the hospital for *three or four* weeks and then you will be able to come home." The old man agreed in a vague, smiling way, looking to his wife for confirmation. She had controlled her tears and was ready to smile when Macmillan, testing the old man's memory, asked him, "What is the street number of your house?" and he replied, "Five shillings." She laughed and said, "That's the rent we used to pay when we moved here fifty years ago."

There was a little more talk and then we rose to leave. Macmillan said, "The ambulance will pick him up at ten o'clock tomorrow morning," but the social worker fell back and took the old lady's arm and said, "Now don't you worry, we'll take good care of him. And don't worry if the ambulance doesn't come until twelve or so—they're often late, but they'll be here." The visit took about twenty minutes altogether.

Notice how economically Macmillan arrives at a conclusion and tells the old couple very specifically what to expect. In a few minutes he had satisfied himself that the patient's mental confusion was caused by his physical condition, and Macmillan had set a time period for dealing with it. The patient had seen the doctor at home, and when later he saw the doctor in the hospital, he should have had confidence that the doctor knew who he was. Macmillan himself was in a position to order diagnostic tests and make nursing suggestions before the patient was admitted. Macmillan had provided continuity to a process that can be bafflingly disjointed. It is interesting also, how in one phrase—"It's not because you haven't been to bed, you know"—he absolved the wife from blame for her husband's admission.

After the visit, Macmillan told us that they would not keep in touch with the wife; if she had trouble, her physician would get in touch with the social worker. He believes that patients and families should solve their own problems as far as they are able, and when they cannot they should be offered what help is needed. As our theory was designed to explain the success of programs like Macmillan's, it is hardly surprising that this whole episode follows our theoretical specifications for milieu therapy fairly closely.

Macmillan's program and a similar one of Querido's in Amsterdam, Holland, are used primarily for deciding upon the appropriate help for each patient. If hospitalization is needed, a patient is likely to accept it as a logical choice if he already has had evidence of the interest and understanding of the people who will be responsible for his care.

Such services are, with few exceptions, unavailable on this continent, but when they are tried, they seem to be successful.* Where they are impossible, we should be able to develop our own techniques for facilitating admission by eliminating delays in hospitalization, by developing more emergency hospitalization, and by using voluntary and informal admissions wherever possible.

ENTERING A HOSPITAL

To enter a new situation among strangers requires alertness, both cognitive and affective.† Probably the newcomer looks first for a role that justifies his presence. This is why admission procedures should be carefully planned; not only does ambiguity tend to increase disorganization, but lack of a role can heighten anxiety and confusion. Even well-organized people can be made to suffer diffusion feelings if they are allowed to wait in unfamiliar places and are not recognized as being there

---

* Variations of this process have been organized at Boston State Hospital and Hudson River State Hospital. More recently, Montefiore Hospital in New York City has developed a similar program.

† See, in this regard, Scheutz's "The Stranger, An Essay in Social Psychology," and Goffman's [3] somewhat different interpretation.

for a legitimate purpose. Feelings of having come to the wrong place, of having been forgotten, of having had one's file lost in the endless red tape of the hospital are all familiar to anyone who has entered any hospital under conditions of mild worry and frustration. The disorganized patient must suffer doubts, fear, confusion, and panic devastating by comparison.

In many hospitals a physician participates in the admission process only to the extent of performing a short physical examination of the patient for the legal protection of the hospital. But by the time a patient is brought to the hospital, he is likely to be suffering from a transition crisis as well as some other psychiatric illness. This, in turn, may be either an acute failure of ego ability in an otherwise adequate personality, or it may be an acute disorganization obscuring longstanding ego deficits. Whether or not a patient is suffering from such deficits, his immediate problem is that, like a migrant, he is a stranger in a strange place. He greatly needs to see an acceptable image of himself reflected in the responses of those with whom he deals and to understand his relationship to this new milieu. In Part II we mentioned various structural aids for keeping the newly admitted patient oriented. Here we shall suggest ways of inducting a patient into a therapeutic milieu that allow him to begin reorganization at the same time that his vulnerability is used to therapeutic ends. The success of military psychiatry in swiftly returning patients with cases of battle fatigue, or acute ego disorganization, to their duties has demonstrated the crucial importance of the early hours in the hospital. Edward Stainbrook [4] believes, for example, that one hour in the first day in the hospital is worth five in the second week. In other words, for many acutely ill people the admission process is a major part of therapy.

Any treatment facility is surrounded by two integuments which a patient must penetrate before he can enter. The first is the legal and administrative layer made up of such matters as eligibility and legality, and the second is a social barrier around the ward or day hospital such as surrounds any system that has an ongoing life of its own.

A patient should be assigned a special "friend" to assist him in maintaining or recovering orientation while crossing the administrative and social boundaries of the new milieu. It is hard to find a name for such a person. At Ville Evrard a social worker called a "hostess" meets every new patient.* William Caudill [5] has described the role of the Japanese *tsukisoi,* or "attendant," who not only accompanies the patient to the hospital but stays with him until he goes home.

Alfred Stanton † in the Boston Veterans' Administration Hospital developed a procedure for minimizing the confusion and disorganization generated by a complex and, to the patient, meaningless admission system; we can abstract from it a four-step initiation procedure of a patient into the therapeutic milieu.

First, support must be quickly available for combating disorientation and disorganization. Stanton trained a pool of aides for this task and assigned them to a roster so that one was always available. When such an aide first meets a new patient, the aide must quickly establish communication so that he can learn enough about the patient to begin confirming the patient's identity. If the aide greets the patient by name and, with a handshake, introduces him to everyone in the room and explains what both they and the patient are doing, it may be sufficient to calm him. Patients who have been tricked into coming to the hospital—or perhaps roughed up by the police—will require more time.

---

* In this country the social worker traditionally concerns herself with the relatives of the patient and does not take an active part in the treatment process. Because social workers do not work on a shift basis, they cannot meet emergencies, and therefore it is unlikely that they will want to undertake this kind of procedure.

† In a personal communication to the authors.

The aide's next step is to find common interests with the patient. For this he must be willing to reveal himself as a person so as to enable the patient in turn to offer himself to the interaction. After having established a relationship, the aide's next duty is to establish the patient's orientation to place and time by finding out how he views the sequence of events leading up to admission. If deception has been used in getting the patient into the hospital, the aide must convince him by his honest explanations that it will play no part in his treatment. As the patient may not fully understand some of the most disorienting deceptions, the aide should help him to reconstruct, as accurately as possible, the critical chain of events.

Ideally, orientation should be established before the legal admission procedures are undertaken. The aide should carry out as many of the procedures as possible himself and accompany the patient through the remainder in order to explain and interpret events to him. The aide's presence will also help to allay the uneasiness of the administrative clerks and to prevent their fear from communicating itself to the patient. The aide might introduce the patient to the examining doctor and, if the patient wishes, remain with him during the examination. When this is over, and the necessary admission formalities are completed, the aide takes the patient to the ward to help him cross the inner boundary of the therapeutic milieu. The time between the front door and the ward should be short; many admission procedures can wait for a few days and be done more conveniently on the ward.*

The aide's fourth and final task is to integrate the patient into the ongoing ward society. To enter a new social system is always difficult, and it can be agonizing to the mentally ill. The

---

* Morgan G. Martin [6] in an instructive and useful monograph has suggested that doctors should have the authority to admit without formality. This is obviously desirable, and when the system permits it, it should be done.

patient should be introduced to the nurse in charge of the ward; she may wish to accompany him while he is being assigned a room or a bed and shown the location of such essentials as the washrooms and dining and day rooms. It is not too many years since a newly appointed social worker, who consented to being admitted to a rather good state hospital as a patient, reported that she only was able to find a bed and blankets through the assistance of other patients. Welcoming committees organized by the ward meeting or patient government can help the new patient to enter the ward social system. These committees will undoubtedly confuse him with some "misinformation"—that is, information that reflects their point of view—but this is one of the prices of the therapeutic milieu. The patients will furnish the newcomer with such useful knowledge as how to get an extra cup of coffee or how to make a phone call. If there is a working alliance between the nurses and the patients, the patient group can convince the new patient of the realities of ward life much more effectively than the staff can.

In hospitals specializing in the treatment of neurotics,* a closely knit ward culture can subvert the incoming patient from staff goals. However, in hospitals taking acutely disorganized patients of any class, sufficient attachment to staff can be developed when the patient is open and available.

The patient should at first be given sources of information rather than the information itself because anxiety usually runs

---

* These hospitals have overdetermined problems. They usually draw patients from the well-to-do levels of society who cannot form social bonds with aides and nurses in the same way that a random selection of the mentally ill population can. In such situations, ward administrators and other professionals may have to take on more active leadership roles. It has been our observation, however, that when wealthy people appear in public facilities in their ordinary proportions, they *do* manage to join the ward society. It is not that they cannot; it is that any homogeneous society tends to become exclusive.

so high that it is not strategic to offer specific information. Ville Evrard's patients produce a booklet for each new arrival with his own, his doctor's, and his social worker's name on the cover. It contains information about the hospital and its major regulations as well as orientation to the geographical features of the hospital.*

All these techniques for admitting the new patient are designed to minimize confusion and ambiguity and maximize structure and clarity so that there are points in the environment around which the patient can crystallize elements of ego organization. When the situation is perfectly clear and his relationship to it clear—provided that he is not suffering from toxic or traumatic disorders—the patient's organization should be maximized. Many variations on this procedure can be equally effective, and, in a sense, each treatment situation has to work out its own procedure.

In general, the admission of the patient should have certain firmly structured, formal characteristics that assure him of his legal and formal identity. In addition, the aide who acts as the patient's friend must mirror back to him what he can learn of his social and personal identity and explain to him the details of what is happening. Routines such as admissions procedures become so commonplace to those who traverse them regularly that considerable thought and sensitivity are needed to understand what they mean to patients.† Discussions on the

---

* Some psychiatrists favor putting the newly admitted patient to bed or giving him a two-day quiet period upon admission. There is a possibility that this allows the patient to work through the transition crisis of hospitalization, but we are inclined to believe that the importance of inducting him into ward life, while he is open and vulnerable, outweighs it.

† "Bureaucracy" is often blamed for the impersonalness of many of its servants. The tendency to get used to any particular routine is a *special problem* for a bureaucracy that undertakes to treat the ill, not an intrinsic evil.

part of the staff with patients who have recently experienced such routines can help to point up their ambiguities and frustrations.

The reluctance of clinical personnel to venture through the inner integument of the hospital system has allowed a number of procedures to develop which, in the name of good business, actually defeat the main purpose of the hospital: the quick and efficient treatment of patients. For example, valuables are usually removed—thus safeguarding the valuables at the expense of the patients. Wedding rings and eyeglasses, or anything worn constantly, should never be taken away since they are so highly egotized as to be almost a part of the self. Most patients can understand that money should be kept in a safe place, but few will be able to understand why a wallet containing pictures of family members should be removed. These pictures, as they so often did in military service, can serve as a connection with the past, a promise for the future, and a medium of exchange in getting to know others in the new environment. Since our sense of the future depends upon our ability to project ourselves, with our egotized objects, forward, it seems likely that retention of familiar things may be vitally related to orientation in time.

In short, an important part of the ward staff's task is to see that a patient keeps things that have symbolic significance for him. Relatives will usually sign releases for valuables if they understand that removing them can be a step toward chronicity; if they will not, the risk of loss must be taken. The danger of a patient commiting suicide or attacking others with such objects is usually grossly exaggerated; a suicidal patient, in any case, can find weapons on any ward if he is entirely intent on killing himself.

An ego insult commonly dealt to new patients is concerned with the manner in which their clothes are handled. Upon a patient's admission, most hospitals mark all of his clothing in order to minimize confusion and loss; sometimes a patient is stripped of his clothing for two or three days. If the patient and aide together can attach the patient's name to his clothes, the process can be, like calling the patient by his name, an identifying, clarifying, and therapeutic maneuver. However, many hospitals literally brand the patient's clothing; these large unsightly marks give a clear message that the patient is not expected to leave the hospital—at least within the lifetime of that garment. Further, such labels place a caste mark upon the patient as indelible as the marking ink.*

Admission problems occur in slightly different forms in day centers and clinics. A newcomer to a clinic, for example, can sit in an agony of doubt wondering if he is in the right place. If he takes a seat and then is afraid to speak to the receptionist, he may be mistaken for a relative of a patient. Such a patient can become alienated or panic stricken and leave without making or keeping his appointment. All new patients must be "recognized"—that is, their identity must be affirmed, their right to be present made overt, and the expectations of their activities in the patient role made clear.

THE MILIEU IN ACTION

The acute hospital as we are describing it is designed to enable the patient to resume social living outside the hospital as quickly as possible. If he has gross ego defects he will need special therapies similar to the work programs that we shall describe in the next chapter. In the acute hospital, the patient's task is to regain ego abilities—especially those related to problems of living in society.

To increase these abilities there must be enough activity

---

* In Kansas City, after considerable ward discussion, markers were bought and clothes were marked, as in laundries, with small identifying signs. Patients and staff worked together to make sure that clothes were identifiable.

on the ward to provide a continuous and changing social situation. Once norms of activity are established, new plans will supplant old ones in a routine way. This is good because any plan, at the period of its inception when arrangements must be made and committees formed, calls for intense and varied interaction. In the meantime the problem for the staff will be the maintenance of an unambiguous structure. Against a ground of organization, a figure of activity can emerge. As we illustrate the kinds of activities that we have found useful and discuss the kinds of problems that arise, it should be remembered that the principles set forth in Part II invariably underlie them.

If admission procedures are adequate and if intensive nursing care can be offered along with appropriate drugs, most patients will recover from acute disorganization in a few days. By this time they should be full-fledged members of the ward society—a society marked by structure, flexibility, and change and with its imperatives laid down in firm rules.

There should be few such firm rules—ten is probably a good symbolic number—and they should be posted on the ward bulletin board. Behavior essential to the running of the ward, such as appearing for ward activities, should be prescribed, and socially disruptive behavior, such as drinking on the ward or absence at times crucial to ward routine, should be proscribed. Penalties should be explicit. On wards that have sufficient freedom it may be difficult to devise appropriate sanctions, and, therefore, multiple infractions of rules may have to result in expulsion of the patient from the hospital. Such a threat is almost always effective even to patients under legal certification. All other violations of the rules should be dealt with by such sanctions and regulations as the ward meetings set up. All nonessential regulations can and should be periodically changed, however. Greenblatt considers this constant flux essential to the therapeutic environment, and as Lee Hanes says about the Kansas City Day Hospital: ". . . just as we are ready to explain our program and describe what goes on, the whole thing changes." [7] There is no doubt that this fluidity often results in an appearance of chaos, but the marks of a bad hospital are silence, order, and apathy. Good hospitals often give an impression of a summer camp during free period.

Delegation of authority to the patient group takes the nurse out of the role of disciplinarian and allows her to play the role of "philosopher, guide, and friend." * It further insures that there will always be plenty of business for the ward meeting. The interchange and debate, the assertion of the self, and the adjustment to others that go on in an active ward meeting are some of the best forms of problem solution available to patients and are thus some of the best opportunities for ego growth.

Although we have emphasized that the individual patient and the patient group should have considerable freedom in choosing what they will do, or what will constitute the activity program, it should remain clear that they *must* do something. If the ward activities are not defined as therapy on the same level as drugs, electric shock, or psychotherapy, it will be difficult for the patient to see why he should become involved in them.

Jordan Scher [8] has described how permissiveness tends to be accompanied either by behavior designed to test limits, and thus to find the implicit social structure, or by avoidance of the responsibility of making decisions in the ambiguous permissive setting. Firm structure does not imply regimentation; it implies, rather, a wide range of available activities and information about the means of carrying them out. The patient or group may choose an activity and, once having chosen it, should expect to be encouraged, urged, and assisted—albeit sparingly

---

* These are the words with which Macmillan describes his social workers. The connotations of "friend" should be taken as "on the patient's side" rather than as the more diffuse "intimate companion."

—to complete it. These activities are the minor crises whose solutions result in ego growth.

Patients initially seem to prefer activities with meaning in terms of their cultural backgrounds, even though they may be in conflict with those backgrounds, because such activities can be apprehended and egotized. Alien activities tend to cause diffusion feelings for the new patient, although he may, as he improves, undertake them for the sake of learning new ways to handle strange environments. Work under realistic circumstances and for appropriate rewards has culturally familiar elements for everyone and is probably the best central activity for all patients, especially men.*

In the Kansas City Receiving Center, a very successful work plan was developed by the patients themselves. This hospital had always lacked funds to buy cigarettes for its patients, most of whom were penniless when they came. Numerous appeals for help had failed to yield a permanent solution. One day when this problem was being discussed at a ward meeting, as it had been many times before, a patient suggested that the group purchase materials from the Occupational Therapy Department, turn them into saleable items, and use the profits for cigarettes for those unable to provide their own. An initial loan of ten dollars from a member of the medical staff put the patients in business. Therapeutically, it was a successful venture. Not only did it give meaning to the activities that had previously been carried on in occupational therapy but it also provided a ramifying need for committees to attend to bookkeeping and sales and so on. As the profits began to come in, committees to see that the cigarettes were equitably distributed had to be formed. The patients were not only dealing adequately and persistently with the instrumental task of

---

* There is a common lay belief that "overwork" causes mental illness. We are inclined to believe that pure overwork can lead to feelings of staleness, futility, and even despair, but not to ego disorganization.

manufacturing but also with such interpersonal problems as control of the patient who did not want to work along with the rest and justice for the ward mate who wanted more than his share of cigarettes. The program reached its high point when the ward group decided to give a patient three dollars to assist him in getting through the first few days after his release from the hospital. The plan was able to survive, without staff interference, for about a year and a half and to surmount such problems as petty theft and the spoiling of materials by confused patients. Its demise can be looked upon as part of the inevitable ebb and flow of ward life.

Such a work project can be just as useful for patients of other social backgrounds. In Chestnut Lodge, a hospital serving wealthy patients, a "kiosk" for the sale of food and cigarettes was successfully built and put into operation by patients.

It is difficult in arranging work programs to convince nurses and other ward staff that they should allow patients to carry them out on their own. Scher (in "Schizophrenia and Task Orientation") has postulated that two forces operate: the manipulative skill many patients have at creating situations where it is easier for others to do things for them than to insist that they do things for themselves; and the high value nurses ascribe to their own practical activity and helpfulness to others. If a nurse does yield to the temptation to do things for a patient, she robs him of an opportunity for ego growth and lowers his self-esteem in the same way that it has been lowered before by his dependency. One new nurse in Kansas City, assigned to a group of patients who were supposed to be choosing a free-period activity, exclaimed in frustration, "By the time they made their decision, the free period was over and they hadn't done a thing." She was missing the central point of milieu therapy.

Work need not be entirely for gain; men are often happy to paint furniture, women to make curtains or bedspreads for the ward. These activities, when they follow a group decision, are particularly good for disorganized people as they have continuity of meaning as well as an accompanying interpersonal reward.

In general, it is profitable to have available, besides work, a number of such activities as discussion groups, athletics or dancing, shopping trips, and outings. Variety contributes to a patient's ability to mobilize ego sets appropriate to the occasion and to enhance his repertoire of ego abilities. If a patient continues to stay with one kind of activity, the staff may persuade him to try others, especially if there is reason to believe that the patient is suffering from ego deficits. However, patients tending toward disperse activities should be encouraged to see one thing through to completion before starting another. This will be an important contribution to ego differentiation for such patients and may mitigate some serious disorders.

TROUBLE SHOOTING

We have prescribed for the therapeutic milieu a structured, flexible activity program, but if we have made it sound like a well-run industry, we have failed to create a true impression. When things are going well, there can be an appearance of chaos; when they are going badly, a sense of apathy creeps in. Very often patients have such diffuse and multiple difficulties that the main task is to keep the milieu sufficiently structured and benign for them to exercise some freedom of action. The ward system will always tend toward disorganization, and at certain periods it may take all of the staff's time to provide an acceptable milieu without attempting to tailor special tasks for individual patients. When a group of patients has improved considerably, it can be recruited to help with newly admitted patients. This situation then gives way to one in which almost all the patients are newly admitted. Hanes has described (in "The Experience of Living in a Day Hospital") how her patients were intensely interested at one phase in projects and activities. Then the group "aged" and incoming patients had difficulty identifying with programs that others had designed. After a period of turmoil the new patients formed committees to study a number of different aspects of ward life, and suddenly the milieu became vital again. The administrator's task in all these changes is to try to keep as good a balance of structure, variety, change, and consistency as he can so that minor crises are continually arising and being resolved.

The ward administrator must be able to guess whether any single problem is an opportunity for ego growth or an obstruction to the program. We do not yet have a typology of problems, and we must therefore rely on rules of thumb arising from a kind of socio-clinical judgment. Even if the doctor has a relationship of trust and confidence with his ward staff, he should make a practice of watching the ongoing flow of ward life just as he would watch the gestures, glances, and monosyllables of a patient in psychotherapy. However, the doctor must appreciate the differences as well as the similarities between ward life as an entity and a patient in psychotherapy. He must learn to mistrust the single dramatic incident and watch instead for regularities. Thus, when one patient attacks another, the doctor will not decide that this reflects the patient's weak ego ability until he has asked himself whether it is not part of a more general restlessness and anxiety. He will ask himself whether or not ward meetings have had "no problems" and whether or not attendance has fallen off because other things "can't be neglected."

It is our impression, following Stanton and Schwartz, that sporadic acting out among patients usually means ambiguities in the communication system. Among staff, the outright complaint of "No one ever tells me anything" is a similar sign. The content of complaints, however, can be misleading because the complainer himself does not always understand what is the matter. For example, a competent aide working in the re-habilitation ward of a state hospital unaccountably began to complain that the patients were no longer improving, although objectively this did not appear to be true. Finally, the aide ad-mitted that she disliked her hours of work. Because she had a special role in the program, she worked from nine to five, the same as the doctors. All other aides worked from six until two or from two until ten. She had gained a so-called "status sign" but had lost all sense of solidarity with her fellow aides, who in turn were sanctioning her in subtle ways. Restoring her to ordinary shift hours brought back her optimism about the patients.

Group acting out often results from an ambiguous au-thority structure or one that is not sufficiently decentralized. When cliques of patients stay out past hours, miss their meals, and skip ward meetings, they are usually testing limits. D. H. Miller [9] has described an episode of group delinquency among adolescent patients placed in an ambiguous therapeutic pro-gram. Relatively straightforward problems such as this can be used in ward meetings as part of the daily program for patients and staff.

Inherent problems of role conflict are another difficulty. We have suggested that sometimes an old nurse whom every-one has been tolerating because she is so close to retirement has been in an intolerable role. If her successor begins to be-have as she did, a role problem is almost certainly involved. Patients, of course, bring different expectations with them to a hospital, and the process of admission must clarify the role structure to each incoming patient. Even so, patients from unusual backgrounds, such as foreign countries or uncommon religious sects, sometimes become confused and must have special explanations made to them.

Another type of role conflict is generated when policy

changes are out of harmony with old patterns of behavior, with the personal ideologies of the staff, or with the imperatives of the situation. Maxwell Jones used newly trained Scandinavian social workers rather than nurses as "social therapists" in his therapeutic community; his nurses found it too hard to assume the equalitarian role that he had developed for the treatment of character disorders. The inexperienced social workers from a different culture had less difficulty. There are many similar examples of the difficulty experienced in persuading ward staff to allow the freedom necessary for new learning to take place. Most mentally ill patients, unfortunately, are cared for in hospitals that are too constricting, too repressive, and too authoritarian.

These suggestions sound simple, but they are not. Just as a psychiatrist trying to understand psychopathology must often hold many apparently unrelated facts in attention for long periods of time, so a ward administrator must often wait for the light to fall on several interwoven difficulties. Sometimes he solves the problem by trial and error, using stratagems suggested by his theoretical knowledge. Even the acknowledgment of failure can lead to resolution if it gives some patient or staff member courage to produce new information about the problem.

In general, problems should be solved at the lowest possible level of the social structure. Most administrators tend to act too much and too often. Like the nurse, the administrator must get more pleasure from seeing others solve problems than from solving them himself. His life is spent inspecting the social fabric of the ward—and only if a thread breaks should he intervene.

THE PRINCIPLE OF INTERPENETRATION

We have indicated that the patient's bonds with the outside world should be maintained throughout his hospitalization so that solutions worked out in the therapeutic milieu can be tried in the natural setting.* This involves striking a balance between the patient's need for unambiguous structure and his need to learn to live with the complexities of the world outside the hospital. For all its complexities, the extra-hospital world contains the egotized objects of the patient's experience, his history, and his social context. Keeping in touch with them can help the patient to integrate the past and project into the future, as well as prevent him from developing too big an investment in the present. If he has had trouble handling the complexity of life outside, he will benefit from solving problems in the hospital, but the real test of his progress will be his ability to succeed in situations in which he has failed before.

The hospital must, therefore, be permeable in both directions. Relatives and friends must be welcome to visit at any reasonable hour, and some ward activities should include them. Understanding of the patient's illness can be enhanced by such intermingling. Parents should always be able to see their children if they wish to; arrangements for this are not so difficult once the need for them is clear.

For many discharged patients their ward mates still in hospital are an important continuity. In Kansas City we found in a ward meeting that many discharged patients had fallen into the habit of visiting the wards and taking part in activities when medical staff were absent. A number of nurses admitted that such patients called them at their homes asking for advice with problems or for support and comfort. We felt that although the nurses' personal involvement should be discouraged, patients should be able to use the hospital as a temporary refuge or support. It was agreed that the nurses should invite the ex-patients to visit and occasionally to have dinner on the ward.

---

* There is a recurring theme throughout our theory of the difference between *in vivo* and *in vitro* learning. This is reminiscent of certain animal experiments in which it was found that habits learned in the field, unlike habits learned in the laboratory, cannot be easily extinguished.

This official recognition of the *status quo* allowed the nurses to discuss the returning patients with ward physicians and sometimes to enlist the help of other staff members in their care. The openness of the system allowed the patient to cut down his dependency on the hospital slowly as he rebuilt his memberships with other groups outside. Later, one evening a week was devoted to drug checks and progress reports, and the patients were encouraged to return to the ward to visit at this time. This use of the hospital ward can be the nucleus of a flexible after-care program.

It is important that the hospital *not* be self-sufficient. Patients should have to leave the hospital for many activities, and the hospital should serve the community in as many ways as it can. At one time the Kansas City Hospital was asked for help in training police recruits to handle the mentally ill. Since almost half the patients had passed through the hands of the police, we welcomed the opportunity, but when a proposal that the recruits be allowed to enter the hospital for one afternoon a week was made to a ward meeting, it met strong opposition. Many patients had had painful experiences with the police. We argued that only a planned program of social interaction with the mentally ill would change their attitudes. The patients gave permission reluctantly and even fearfully, but when the recruits arrived the next week they were so uncomfortable that the patients were both relieved and amused at the irony of the situation. Eventually the patients took pity on the recruits and tried to put them at ease. A normal social atmosphere developed, and from table tennis and baseball they gradually drifted into discussion, sometimes about the patients' experiences with the police.* The patient group eventually became involved in the training program and worked hard to

---

* The police were amazed to hear how they had been perceived. One patient explained to a recruit that when he had seen the policeman with his gun, he had been convinced that the Communists were getting him at last.

plan the policemen's shift on the ward for them. Some of these patients had never passed any but frightened or angry words with the police in their lives; to engage in social exchanges with them was an important ego asset, hopefully contributing complexity to their perception of authority. Furthermore, planning and carrying out the activities of the shift was a successful resolution of rather complex instrumental and socio-emotional problems intimately connected with both the hospital and the outside world.

THE PROCESS OF DISCHARGE

Leaving the acute hospital is more rational than entering it. The staff have had time to assess the patient and balance his needs against the demands society is likely to place upon him. Hospital care should be ended as soon as possible because, besides being expensive, for some reason not yet clear there is a tendency for longer stays in hospital to be associated with a higher relapse rate regardless of illness, age, or hospital type.[10] An expectation of discharge should be built into the norms of the ward; even so, it may be nearly as difficult to leave the hospital as to enter it. It is often valuable to set a definite date as a goal; some patients improve remarkably with this stimulation.

Some patients tend to have recurrences of symptoms or anxiety attacks as their time of discharge approaches. These patients are often referred to as "dependent on the hospital," but they are probably better thought of as being unsure of themselves. The high number of requests for discharge that follow visits home probably indicate that ego abilities have more currency than patients anticipate. If the hospital is sufficiently open, there should be little need for special confirmation of this sort. If such symptoms occur, the patient can be suspected of having some unresolved ego disabilities or even deficits.

Sometimes it is advisable for patients to resume major portions of their usual lives before permanently leaving the therapeutic milieu. The day hospital is useful, particularly for women who should take up their relationships with their families again, whereas the night hospital can allow men to return to work and to visit their families. In this way patients can resume their major roles while still living in a protected situation, and the potentialities of a mild transition crisis can be used for ego growth.

A patient should not be handed like a chattel from one agency to another in the after-care process. Agencies involved with a patient before he is hospitalized and those who will help him afterwards should be encouraged to visit while the patient is in the hospital. Social agencies have a crucial role to play in rehabilitation because ego restoration will be of little use if the extra-hospital milieu does not provide an arena for action. For example, a newly acquired ability to work may lead to marked diffusion feelings and subsequent disorganization if there is no job to turn to upon discharge.

In summary, interpenetration means that the hospital's responsibility for the patient does not end with the decision to discharge. If hospitalization is regarded as a joint effort of patient and staff to achieve better functioning for the patient, it may lead to wider cooperative association among the patient, his family, helping agents in the community, and the hospital.

ALTERNATIVE METHODS OF TREATING
ACUTE ILLNESS

It is implicit in our discussion that there are a number of loci for treating patients ranging from full hospitalization to out-patient treatment.* It is hard to make a rational choice of treatment because of two underlying but contradictory assump-

---

* See, for example, the work of Carmichael.[11]

tions shared by almost everyone and related to the inherent conflict over support and control of deviant behavior. These assumptions are, first, that all severely disordered patients are dangerous or in danger and, therefore, must go into the hospital, and, second, that hospitalization is somehow inherently damaging because it confirms the severity and perhaps the irreversibility of the illness. These beliefs tend to obscure the appropriate decision even when it is obvious that it should be made entirely on the basis of the patient's relationship to his milieu.

In general, full hospitalization for a short time seems to be needed by patients with major ego disorganization or superego deficits and patients whose situations are extremely disorganized or ambiguous. It may be strategic to hospitalize patients who deny their illness, or whose families do so, for a short period of time so that they can be brought under normative control outside the home.

Longer terms of full hospitalization are probably indicated for people who have lost social control or have severe ego disorders of the type usually associated with synthetic function failure. These include marked aggressiveness, severely disordered or impulsive behavior, and suicidal impulses. Still longer hospitalization may be needed for those with ego defects unless appropriate rehabilitation programs are available on an out-patient basis.

For the whole group of intermediate cases, including psychotics with moderate disorganization, there is evidence that full hospitalization is not needed. The reasons for avoiding full hospitalization are numerous as implied in the discussion above. Briefly, the full removal of the patient from his milieu tells him that he cannot control himself and is a blow to his self-esteem. The day hospital provides a better arena for solution of graded problems at the same time that the patient maintains his outside contacts. In this way his progress in both places can be watched and his hospital routine designed to fill the gaps in his competence at home. Such a program allows the patient to effect changes in his home milieu as he learns new ways of meeting social demands. His hours in the hospital can be reduced as he improves, and his transition can be accomplished without the diffusion feelings and even grief that sudden separation from the hospital can sometimes cause, especially to patients with few outside resources.

A word should be said about psychiatric wards of general hospitals. Although they are increasingly popular, milieu programs cannot be developed in them unless the hospital agrees to have a ward administrator with authority to include the patients in mandatory activity.

In general, the decision to move from the more conservative hospitalization to a freer home care should become more common when we can distinguish sooner and better between ego deficit and ego disorganization and when our control of the worst symptoms with drugs is refined. Such a decision will be in keeping with the tradition of medical practice.

References

[1] A. QUERIDO, "Early Diagnosis and Treatment Services," *The Elements of a Community Mental Health Program* (New York: Milbank Memorial Fund Publication, 1956).

[2] DUNCAN MACMILLAN, *Community Mental Health, The Mapperley Hospital Scheme,* special supplement to *Canada's Mental Health* (Ottawa, Canada: n.d.). Copies available from Mental Health Division, Department of National Health and Welfare, Ottawa, Canada.

[3] ERVING GOFFMAN, *The Presentation of Self in Everyday Life,* Monograph 2 (Edinburgh, Scotland: University of Edinburgh, Social Sciences Research Center, 1956).

[4] EDWARD STAINBROOK, in a lecture given before the members of the Department of Psychiatry, Dalhousie University, Halifax, Canada.

[5] WILLIAM CAUDILL, "Around the Clock Patient Care in Japanese Psychiatric Hospitals: the Role of the Tsukisoi," *American Sociological Review,* 26 (April 1961), 204.

[6] MORGAN G. MARTIN, *The Mental Ward—A Personnel Guidebook* (Springfield, Ill.: Charles C. Thomas, 1962).

[7] LEE D. HANES, "The Experience of Living in a Day Hospital" (paper read to the Ontoanalytic Society, Chicago, 1961).

[8] JORDAN M. SCHER, "Schizophrenia and Task Orientation: The Structured Ward Setting," *A.M.A. Archives of Neurology and Psychiatry,* 78 (1957), 531-538.

[9] D. H. MILLER, "The Etiology of an Outbreak of Delinquency in a Group of Hospitalized Adolescents," in M. Greenblatt, D. J. Levinson, and R. H. Williams (eds.) *The Patient and the Mental Hospital* (Glencoe, Ill.: Free Press, 1957), p. 427.

[10] HENRY BRILL and ROBERT E. PATTON, "Clinical-Statistical Analysis of Population Changes in New York State Mental Hospitals since Introduction of Psychotropic Drugs" (paper read to the 117th Annual Meeting of the American Psychiatric Association, May 10, 1961).

[11] DONALD M. CARMICHAEL, "A Psychiatric Day-Hospital for Convalescent Patients," *Mental Hospitals* (January 1960).

CHAPTER 11

Work

THE RELEVANCE OF WORK FOR EGO INTEGRITY

Work was recognized as a central therapy by those most successful of practitioners, the nineteenth century inventors of moral treatment. It can be the most important' single activity in the hospital, and it is a culturally valued occupation throughout the Western world; to fail at it is to be stigmatized as incompetent. Even those of ample means are seldom idle; there is no longer a truly leisured elite. Maxwell Jones [1] has commented:

There seems to be a fundamental human need to make use of mind and body in a constructive way. To afford a man the opportunity to do this, particularly if in the process he acquires new skills, would seem to add to his self-esteem. The factor of accomplishment seems to be particularly important and appears to give the individual a feeling of control over his environment.*

Occupation is such an important part of self concept that almost all normal adult males would list their occupation if

---

* Notice how similar to Robert White's "competence" this sounds.

they were asked to describe themselves. Two strangers falling into conversation and seeking a common ground of understanding often ask each other's occupation. A man's occupation will probably predict a greater percentage of his behavior than any other fact that can be known about him.

Work as therapy is both old and successful. Chronic schizophrenics with long histories of deterioration have been successfully rehabilitated and even returned to society through programs built around occupational retraining.

D. H. Bennett and R. K. Freudenberg [2] report that following industrial rehabilitation, a group of patients, with an average hospital stay of eight years, have been successfully returned to work and stabilized in the community. These patients had hitherto proved impervious to all other available therapies and were, therefore, considered technically disabled. Such patients have a negligible chance of successful rehabilitation under ordinary circumstances.

We can account for these facts partly on the basis of increased self-esteem on the part of the patient. But further than this, working requires directing continued attention and effort to a task that is often repetitive and for which the criteria of success are usually clear. These circumstances suggest that the restorative power of work may be related to the accumulation of new, well-differentiated ego sets.

In addition, work provides a milieu in which the elementary social skills can be relearned as a by-product. This means that as attention is not primarily focused upon them there can be a wider toleration of temporary deviance.

There is evidence that work, paid for at reasonable rates, carried out under pleasant, realistic, unambiguous conditions, and organized into a graded series of tasks * through which a

---

* Work is a natural activity for grading, and this, too, makes it useful for the therapeutic milieu.

patient can progress as he improves, greatly increases the chances of his leaving the hospital and remaining stabilized in the community. We suggest that this is because work, under such conditions, involves specific skills carried out in affectively neutral contexts and leading to rewards of esteem and approval. These activities can be expected to favor the development of relatively strong, well-differentiated, and easily mobilized ego sets that are fairly immune from spreading, both because they are repeatedly reinforced and because their neutrality minimizes the likelihood of strong affects and unpleasant ego feelings becoming attached to them.

WORK AND SOCIAL COMPETENCE

Whether inside a hospital or outside, success at work goes beyond the mere mastery of sufficient technical skill to perform the task at hand; it comprehends sufficient socio-emotional skill for the worker to relate to and become a part of the group of his fellow workers. Both the instrumental and socio-emotional aspects of work are important to its therapeutic potential. It seems probable, though, that the instrumental aspects are intrinsically less demanding and, therefore, easier to perfect. However, even instrumental competence presupposes an ability to conform minimally to the rules surrounding the work situation, as well as sufficient accuracy and speed to satisfy production requirements. Socio-emotional competence, however, *requires* that a patient be able to learn the norms of the working group, conform to them, and perhaps use group interaction for its tension-lowering function. We shall, however, emphasize the essential unity of these two aspects of work, because in practice it is seldom possible to separate them.

Ferguson [3] describing a sheltered workshop for the severely physically disabled says:

Much of the credit for the friendly and happy atmosphere of the factory must be attributed to the men themselves. The team spirit was extraordinarily well developed. The men clearly recognized that they were not all endowed with equal capacity for work, but they were prepared to work as a team and to help each other as far as possible.

Much earlier, Mayo had demonstrated that among an ordinary factory work group there was a wide divergence in the rate of production.* When asked to estimate their own production rate, however, all workers tended to cite the group mean; group unity apparently made it essential to obscure differences.

In short, it appears that instrumental success is not entirely sufficient for occupational success. Membership in a working group is equally important, and a patient must possess communicative and social skills sufficient to attain this membership. It even seems amply documented that once a person achieves group membership he will be carried even though he produces less than his share, whereas if he does not achieve membership even overproduction will be resented.

The division of labor in an industrial society creates a need for a worker to possess relational skills over and above the level required for technical efficiency so that he can understand group decisions about the allocation of work, the most efficient ways to carry it out, and which of management's demands are reasonable. It is in this ability to deal minimally with the complexities of the group interaction that many patients fail.

Work presents opportunities for ego growth to all patients; even those with adequate work skills can add complexity to their instrumental organizations and clarification to their socioemotional ones. For chronic patients who have been desocialized by long stays in a hospital, and for newly admitted patients with long histories of occupational inadequacy, it is

---

* For a description of Mayo's work, as well as for a lucid account of the beginnings of industrial sociology, see the work of Brown.[4]

the treatment of choice. Many of the techniques employed will be similar for these two occupationally impaired groups, but desocialized patients will require preparatory resocialization.

PREPARING THE DESOCIALIZED PATIENT
FOR WORK

The desocialized chronic patient represents a heritage from pre-drug-treatment days, and we can expect him eventually to disappear. We shall digress, however, to discuss briefly the reason for this. Although the number of admissions to hospitals increases each year, the number of discharges increases proportionately; but the proportion of the group of discharged patients who relapse and return to a hospital remains constant at about thirty-seven per cent. The psycho-pharmaceutical drugs are creating a new mental hospital, one with a huge population rotating through its wards fairly rapidly. Many ego-damaged people have multiple problems: poor employment histories, difficulties in physical health, and socially impoverished lives. The acute psychotic episode is often only one more difficulty in a life beset with difficulties. Yet the psychotic episode with its resulting hospitalization is a marker that forces this patient to our attention. At one time the occupationally inadequate patient tended to remain in the chronic ward of a hospital where his difficulties were of little moment, but today, if his incapacities are not faced, he becomes a major community problem.

As we have emphasized, the ability to work and to hold a job is one of the important prerequisites for a stable life outside a mental hospital. In the past, much of the ex-patient's occupational difficulty was blamed on the prejudice of employers—that is, on the stigma of mental illness. In our own research we have found that fifty per cent of a group of discharged patients wanting to work were still unemployed a year after their release from the hospital. In another study we found one-third of a sample of a thousand discharged patients to have been on the rolls of the department of public welfare either before or after hospitalization.* Prejudice against the ex-patient is not a sufficient explanation of these figures, and Simon Olshansky,[5] in a pioneering inquiry into the problems met by a sample of discharged patients in obtaining work in the Boston area, has a more rational explanation. From a series of consecutively discharged men he eliminated those who were over forty-five years of age or of a racial origin that might invite prejudice. The remainder of the patients were followed into the community. Those patients who had had good work histories before they went to the hospital were able to find work quite easily after discharge; those whose working records had been erratic or inadequate did not, by and large, find work. It seems from this that an employer is less concerned with a history of mental illness than with an unsatisfactory work history.

Because of the interdependence of the instrumental and socio-emotional aspects of work, inability to conform to group norms † may be as important a reason for an unsatisfactory work history as inefficiency in the purely technical aspects of a job. Furthermore, failure to achieve some acceptance by the working group is likely to result in resignation or discharge.

Norms are developed through interaction, and in a work group they are a distillate of day-to-day experience. Seldom written down, they are, nevertheless firm. For example, nurses and attendants have unwritten rules about what type of patient it is appropriate to care for on any particular ward, about what

---

* Studies are in progress at the Mental Health Research Unit, New York State Department of Mental Hygiene, Syracuse, New York.

† The early work of Elton Mayo and the elaborations of his work by Homans (see *The Human Group*) and by Roethlisberger and Dickson [6] have demonstrated beyond a doubt that the norms of the working group are a major force in the maintenance of production rates.

things shall and shall not be charted, about what may be done for patients without consultation with the doctor, about security and patient freedom, about how much nurses can be expected to do in one working day, and about where particular problems can be taken for solution. It is rare for the work norm accepted by the group to be precisely the same as management's formal rules. If a new worker accepts the standards of the work group, and his fellow workers accept him, a great deal of his conduct is controlled by a series of cues as to whether his behavior is appropriate. If he is able to anticipate the group's demands upon him and receive approval, he will be quite central to the group's functioning. At the other extreme, if he does not seem to be able to respond to the group's expectations, the group cannot control his actions and he will tend to drift to the periphery. The giving and receiving of sanctions and the getting and giving of support account for about one-third of the activity in a task-oriented small group * and the members must be minimally aware of this process.

In the light of all this, it is easy to see why the ex-patient must have both kinds of work skills. The schizoid ex-patient is particularly disadvantaged because of his poorly developed interpretive sets resulting, in turn, in impaired affective symbolic communication and apparent flatness of affect. All these deficits make it difficult for him to perceive cues, and his tendency to withdraw from the web of interaction exacerbates this deficiency.

Because of the dual demands of the work situation, patients who have lost their social skills must be rehabilitated both socially and occupationally before having to face the complexities of the working world. The first step is probably the creation on the wards of artificial groups. These groups should be no larger than twelve patients, and they should be held as

---

* See, in this connection, "The Equilibrium Problem in Small Groups," in Parsons and Bales, *The Working Papers.*

constant in their composition as possible. They should be under the care and supervision of a single psychiatric aide with whom they should work, eat, and spend their leisure hours.* These groups will almost certainly meet dozens of unforeseen problems. For example, the groups will contain patients who have various degrees of freedom of movement within the hospital because some patients will be thought to need more security than others, and members may be assigned to different meal hours. Many such interruptions will arise to threaten the group's integrity, but it is basic and must be adhered to. Ideally the group should only be broken up when more than half of its members have been discharged.†

It does not matter too much what these resocialization groups do as long as they do something with meaning. The aim of an aide leading a group on a ward where there are many incontinent patients may be to get his patients clean and tidy.

---

* If there are obvious groupings already in existence, these may be followed in developing the therapeutic units. If not, the suggestions of the aides and nurses as to the group compositions should be sought. Spontaneous associations on the ward should be encouraged by placing friends in the same groups. The group should be assigned to one nurse or aide who will have responsibility for instituting an activity program and who will spend as much of his working day as possible with it. If it can be arranged, and if staffing is adequate, the aide should be assigned to only one group. If insufficient staff is available, aides can be assigned to two separate groups, each for half of his working day. If there is still not enough staff available to involve all the patients in a group situation, it may be necessary to neglect some temporarily. It is often efficient to group two or three wards together as a working unit. One person can then take care of paper work and such tasks as the ordering and obtaining of supplies for all of the wards. Furthermore, on some wards aides are constantly busy, whereas on others there are peak activity periods. Grouping a number of wards together may enable better scheduling of the nurses' and aides' time.

† In Weyburn Hospital when we first started patients' groups, the attendants were anxious to "promote" individual patients to better wards as they improved. The attendants soon realized, however, that patients tended to relapse when they were removed from their groups and put among strangers on wards that they experienced as different rather than better.

On a pre-discharge ward one of the aims of the group may be, through group discussion and study, to plan the strategy of returning to the outside world. Some may be primarily working groups, others primarily recreational.

The most important product of this kind of program is that if one aide is assigned to a small group of patients, it is very difficult for the aide to keep himself from *learning something about them as people in the strictly human sense.* He begins to see them as people in the *role* of patients rather than as irrevocably patients. The patients, also, begin to know one another in a new way, and, since their group is artificially maintained, they may form a number of personal ties over a period of time. These results will be greatly accelerated if the aide understands the object of the group activity and is able to participate in it with interest and imagination.

The aide perhaps should be taught first that the basic reason for deterioration of patients in large hospitals is that their illness makes it difficult for them to initiate group relationships and the hospital has done nothing to help them. Thus, the patient becomes isolated; he has no group memberships and he feels no compulsion to conform to group norms. The aide should be taught that all patients, even the most psychotic, will respond in some degree to social pressures. Especially will they try to conform to the standards of a group of which they are a member, and, therefore, if an aide forms a group and interacts intimately with this group, the norms that emerge will be likely to conform to his standards of behavior. Once the group has developed to the point where it has some cohesion and is no longer just a collection of individuals, the members will lend support to one another in times of stress.

Early group activities can be focused on making the patients aware of one another and encouraging them to communicate with one another. A number of simple activities can be performed in ways that promote the patients' awareness of one another. For example, a group of patients can each be called upon to imitate a letter of the alphabet which has been written on the blackboard by the aide.* If only one piece of chalk is used, its transfer among the patients forces their attention onto one another. From this the patients can graduate to writing the alphabet, with each patient writing one letter in the series. Increasingly complex activities, such as the writing of names and addresses, can logically end in traditional spelling bees—with which patients seem to deal surprisingly well.

A technique for increasing interactional proficiency is the continuous translation of feeling reactions into cognitive verbal terms as we have suggested above. Thus, if a work team is carrying bricks, and a patient is not carrying his share, instead of calling out, "Come on, pull your weight," an aide can say, "It's making me and some of the others angry to see that you are carrying fewer bricks than they are. We think that everybody should carry just about the same number of bricks unless there is a real reason why he can't do it." This is a translation into entirely intellectual terms of the metacommunications that go along with the more natural sort of message. Using this technique in all sorts of situations seems to help patients to learn what is expected of them in a group situation, and they gradually seem to need less obvious cues to guide them. We can summarize the process of preparing chronic or inadequate patients for work in three simple but basic rules: First, maximize all aspects of group living; second, maximize the opportunities for social interaction in everything that goes on in the ward; third, learn to talk a new language to the patients in which affective metacommunications are explicit in clear cognitive terms rather than implicit in the emotional cues.

---

* This technique was described by R. J. Corsini in a seminar at the University of Kansas Medical School, Department of Psychiatry, 1957.

We have given only a few illustrations of exercises in social rehabilitation. Most nurses and ward aides can think of many more.

Work programs aimed at rehabilitating the patient and not at exploiting him in hospital industries are relatively rare in America. Peter Peffer [7] was one of the first to report a work program in which patients were paid. He hired three patients into one job in his Veterans' Administration Hospital and split up the salary accordingly. He believed that the incentive of money was of such importance that it would induce patients to give up their habits of isolation. Later reports on work projects have come from George Brooks,[8] David Landy and Harry Raulet,[9] and Carmichael (see "A Psychiatric Day-Hospital for Convalescent Patients"). Jean Dorgan [10] has reported on the industrial programs of a number of British hospitals—for example, Glenside Hospital near Bristol, where 400 out of 1,100 patients were employed in industrial therapy within the hospital.

NETHERNE HOSPITAL—A MODEL PROGRAM

Netherne Hospital, referred to earlier, reported in 1960 that 1,457 of 1,822 patients were employed. Of these, 51 per cent worked for wages in the hospital utilities, 25 per cent were occupied at handicrafts, 22 per cent worked in industrial workshops, and 1.7 per cent were employed outside the hospital. The hospital supplies a diversity of industrial work requiring widely different skills.*

Patients work five hours a day and are required to dress neatly, be on time, punch a time clock, and learn the general

* These include office jobs; record keeping; typing; printing; typesetting; collating; stitching; lettering; bookbinding; manufacture of aprons, cushions and deck chairs; dismantling; assembling of screwdrivers, saws, drills, car handles, boxes; finishing of dominoes, duster dolls, electric blankets; drill inspection; packaging of bon-bons and toilet articles.

norms of the occupational world. At the same time, they are part of a social rehabilitation program organized around their free-time activities.

In spite of this quite famous program, Freudenberg and Bennett have recently estimated about 10 per cent of their chronic patient group as totally disabled. John Wing * in experimental studies at Netherne reported that for certain chronic patients encouragement by a staff group leader resulted in increased production, but this production returned to base when the stimulation was removed. It is crucial, in our view, that in this experiment the task of patient stimulation was never delegated to the work group. To do so might have resulted in the development of rudimentary work norms. We find ourselves in the theoretical position of postulating that an attempt to develop group cohesiveness and work norms among this group might have reduced the percentage with irreversible ego damage. In other words, among the more severely impaired patients, the failure to maintain performance need not necessarily be interpreted as the basic substrate of schizophrenia. Nevertheless, irreversible loss of sets may have occurred in some cases of long neglect. Normal work performance should probably not be a goal of work programs until at least the rudiments of the ability to relate to others in a group are learned.

Netherne's program for the psychiatrically disabled, nevertheless, is the most complete that we have seen and we shall describe it briefly.

All work is carried out in pleasant but realistic situations. A simple task that many patients start with is the disassembling of telephone relays and the sorting of the parts for use in repairs or as scrap. Wires are removed from their connections, screws are undone, and as patients reduce these complex pieces of

---

* In a personal communication to the authors.

equipment to their component parts, others sort them into bins for redistribution. There is continuing contact with the out-side world as trucks arrive with new raw material and take away the completed work. The most desocialized patients start here. They work slowly and inefficiently, but the work takes place in a social context, and some of the patients increase their skills. Eventually most of them earn significant sums of money. If they improve, they are moved to more difficult tasks.*

At the other end of the work scale is the printing shop. Here, with modern printing, assembling, and bookbinding equipment, patients operate at a level adequate for the outside world. The factory has facilities for learning new skills, and the whole operation competes in the open market. This shop does much of the printing for hospitals in the London area and produces forms, reports, and letterheads. It provides complex tasks similar to those that the patients will have to cope with outside.

These two operations are the ends of a scale of graded tasks to which the patients are carefully fitted. At the same time as they increase their instrumental skill they are encouraged to undertake more active social arrangements. Finally, the patients are taught many simple facts about the outside world—which for many have changed dramatically while they have been in the hospital—and after careful evaluation by all staff who know them,† the patients are readied for discharge.

There are several ways for patients to leave the hospital. A few work outside and return at night. Some go to centers run

---

* At Weyburn Hospital we would not have moved patients individu-ally in the way that Netherne does. The use of the group as a therapeutic tool is more developed in North America than in Britain, and this may be a national difference.

† Netherne considers its evaluation program the key to its remark-able success with chronic patients. All patients are evaluated at regular conferences by everyone who has any contact with them, thus capitalizing upon everybody's knowledge of them.

by the Department of Labour for further training. Some go to sheltered workshops, and others apply for employment under the British Government's provisions for disabled workers. Some patients are able to compete in the open labor market. Their living arrangements are also carefully worked out: some go to hostels, some to lodging houses, and others to relatives. Netherne tries to equip each patient with a maximum of social and occupational skills and then to see that he is neither overplaced nor underplaced. Netherne's follow-up program is equally flexible: the patient may come back to the hospital, and some may be seen at the factory gate, at home, or even in a pub. Furthermore, anyone from aide to doctor may follow him, depending on the individual patient's needs. It is paradoxical that although staffs of many large hospitals complain that their patients are invisible to society and hence forgotten, they have allowed their ex-patient to become invisible to them. Freudenberg and Bennett have found a cure for this differential blindness through their flexible follow-up program.

In America, we have tended to think of occupational rehabilitation as a task to be undertaken after the patient is discharged from the mental hospital, if at all. In this way we lose the therapeutic potential of the work program and prolong the length of time in which the patient is idle. However, as we have stated above, this situation is changing because of the much higher rate of return to the community of first-admitted patients. We are, however, increasing our pools of inadequate and unemployable people who at one time would have found their way to chronic wards, and this problem will eventually have to be faced in the community.

References

[1] MAXWELL JONES, *Rehabilitation in Psychiatry* (WHO Publication, 1952, in mimeo from Department of National Health and Welfare, Ottawa, Canada).

[2] D. H. BENNETT and R. K. FREUDENBERG, *Rehabilitation in Psychiatry* (Netherne Hospital, South Coulsdon, England, in mimeo); see also JOHN K. WING and G. W. BROWN, "Social Treatment of Chronic Schizophrenia: A Comparative Survey of Three Mental Hospitals," *The Journal of Mental Science,* 107, No. 450 (1961), 847-861.

[3] T. FERGUSON, "The Idea of the Sheltered Workshop," *Occupational Therapy and Rehabilitation,* 29 (April 1950), 81.

[4] J. A. C. BROWN, "The Social Psychology of Industry" (Baltimore: Penguin Books, 1954).

[5] SIMON OLSHANSKY, and others, *Survey of Employment Experiences of Patients Discharged from Three State Mental Hospitals During Period 1951-1953* (in mimeo, April 1959).

[6] F. J. ROETHLISBERGER and WILLIAM J. DICKSON, *Management and the Worker* (Cambridge, Mass.: Harvard University Press, 1950).

[7] PETER A. PEFFER, "Money: a Rehabilitation Incentive for

Mental Patients," *American Journal of Psychiatry*, 110 (August 1953).

8 GEORGE W. BROOKS and others, "The Vermont Story" (privately published at Vermont State Hospital, Waterbury, Vt.).

9 DAVID LANDY and HARRY RAULET, "The Hospital Work Program" in M. Greenblatt and B. Simon (eds.) *Rehabilitation of the Mentally Ill* (Washington, D.C.: American Association for the Advancement of Science, 1959).

10 JEAN DORGAN, "Observations on Industrial Therapy in United Kingdom Mental Hospitals," supplement to *Canada's Mental Health* (Ottawa: Department of National Health and Welfare, n.d.).

CHAPTER 12

The Community

It is harder to structure a therapeutic milieu in a natural setting than in a hospital because we have so little control over the forces in play upon a patient. There are many reasons for this; the milieu has no clear boundaries, and the numerous influences in it cannot all be comprehended. In addition, we have not yet studied these influences very deeply, preferring to concentrate our attention upon the ego damage itself—to the neglect of the field in which it was sustained. As a result we have an immense literature about patients but only a small one about the situations in which they acquired this role. Consequently, we have little power to intervene in the milieu.

What is worse, much of our information about the social contexts in which ego-damaged patients are found is in a form that we cannot readily use. We assume, and our theory is based upon this assumption, that the appearance and the course of these disorders are associated in important, if poorly understood, ways with conditions in systems of social interaction—more particularly such influential systems as the family, the school, and the working group. However, our knowledge of the occurrence of ego disorders is largely tied to such things as census tracts,[1] social class,[2] and ethnic groups,[3] and we have to infer the characteristics of the systems in which the deviance occurs. More recently, factors such as loneliness, unsociability, and isolation [4, 5] have been investigated and, although they seem more relevant, they too, like the concrete variables, are *products* of interaction systems and, therefore, are indexes rather than attributes.*

Nevertheless, some studies have thrown indirect light upon the community's therapeutic potential. For example, the discovery that neuroses are, by and large, self limiting (see Shepherd and Gruenberg, "The Age for Neuroses") suggests that most milieus offer support and challenge sufficient for ego restitution. In view of this it is not surprising that we sometimes find clinically that good results follow manipulation of what appear to be crucial forces in social systems.† We shall suggest here what kinds of manipulations are possible, discuss in some detail the ways in which the family, as a type of social system, appears to be related to the occurrence of some mental illnesses, and speculate where certain therapeutic milieus for the ego-damaged patient might be found in the community.

SOME THERAPEUTIC MANEUVERS

Creating a therapeutic milieu in the community is like participating in a judo match: forces that cannot be altered are used for a new purpose. There seem to be three basic ways

---

*An additional problem with the interpretations of these studies is that, being correlational, they are based on modal findings, whereas events in social systems are patterned and require understanding of the relationship among all the variables. This method of analysis has led us to ignore the plausible alternative interpretations.

† These forces may already be doing the work of restitution; they may, however, have nothing to do with recovery—other unsuspected elements of the situation may be in operation in any given case. Only research can throw light on these problems.

of doing this: first, someone in the milieu can act upon the therapist's advice and thus be his agent; second, someone can be added to the milieu or removed from it, thus changing the nature of the relationships within the milieu; and third, such supports as training or extra facilities and resources can be added to the system.

In using someone as the therapist's agent, the situation must be fairly clearly understood, and the system must be relatively small in order that the therapist's agent can have the predicted effect. For example, just after the war some returning servicemen found that children they had been looking forward eagerly to seeing appeared to resent their presence in the household and caused conflict between them and their wives. This was especially true of boys between the ages of five and ten. A program was worked out for the boys that was actually based on an idea that the boys had failed to solve the Oedipal crisis but would probably be able to do so if they were given a chance. Accordingly, the fathers were given the following advice: "Take the boy with you wherever you possibly can. Do not take your wife, just the boy, and it doesn't much matter what you do as long as just the two of you do it. Come back in a month and let me know what happens." This was remarkably successful in breaking up the child's alliance with his mother. When we analyze the situation, we see that the psychiatrist acted in the role of physician to the father advising him to try a procedure that would at least do no harm. For the boy, however, this resulted in a change in milieu and gave him an opportunity to solve the problem of how to relate to his father without having his mother present to protect him during setbacks. Furthermore, father-son roles can be worked out and norms governing them developed in this small subsociety. It is perhaps important to note that this didactic maneuver was not in any traditional sense a psychiatric therapy, inasmuch as the psychiatrist used neither a transference relationship nor insight. By the same token it cannot be called casework, as that also is essentially a dyadic verbal relationship with the goal of helping the client to find solutions to his problems.* It was, instead, a process in which the father was used as the therapist's agent to change the child's milieu and allow him to develop new ego organizations that included a relationship with the father.

In one sense this is a simple "common-sense" counseling method. However, when knowledge of the theory of social systems lies behind the prescription, it ceases to be a common-sense move and becomes a part of the body of skills that we are calling milieu therapy. That this body is very slight is pointed up by our selection of a child with a temporary problem as an example of the use of the therapeutic milieu in the community. We have not yet used such a technique with a psychotic patient.

The second maneuver is the introduction of someone new into a milieu, the removal of someone from it, or the altering of its boundary conditions. An example of the first was worked out by a colleague † for the treatment of autistic children. He prescribed the addition of a good-natured, feeble-minded girl of eighteen years to a family group as a constant companion to the autistic child. He reasoned that a mildly defective girl would be able to maintain interaction with the child because she would not be dismayed by his deviant behavior and his low level of feedback. He assumed that the constant interaction would help the child to get in contact with others. Furthermore, the presence of the "sitter" would allow the distraught mother to withdraw some of her attention from the child. This use of the persistent, outgoing, uncritical characteristics of a mildly defective girl proved effective. We assume, moreover, that interacting with such a girl in a clinic or day center would not have

---

* This is a paraphrase of a definition given by Helvi Boothe, for many years Director of Social Services for the Menninger Foundation.

† William F. Hanley, now a practitioner in Calgary, Alberta, Canada

been so effective because the intense relationship between the mother and the child could not have been so diluted. As it was, the whole social and psychological field was altered.

Macmillan and Lionel Cosin [6] both remove senile patients from their homes for short periods as a therapeutic maneuver. To take them into the hospital for "holidays" seems to enable relatives to endure the stress of caring for them, because the relatives can anticipate periodic respites. On the surface, this looks as if the milieu therapy was being dispensed to the relatives, but in fact their tranquillity is necessary if the senile patient is not going to be confused and irrational.

The changing of the boundary conditions around a social system is often advised on a common-sense basis: middle-aged women are advised to go to work, overprotective mothers are advised to allow their youngsters more freedom to come and go unsupervised, and fathers are advised to try to get a job that does not include traveling. There are good theoretical reasons why all these changes should work, and we can anticipate that eventually their efficacy will be more firmly established.

The third general category of intervention into the milieu is the addition of some needed concrete support—sometimes through other agents. Such things as removal of a family from a slum to public housing can, on a common-sense basis, break up vicious circles of deviance. It is said that the ambulance teams who give continuous emergency service to the City of Amsterdam always carry money and that they very often find that an acutely psychotic patient can be calmed by the immediate resolution of a financial crisis. Social workers serving slum areas have told us that in many cases immediate concrete services, such as getting new shoes for the children or medical care for the mother, can restore a temporarily disorganized situation.

We shall now turn to a consideration of the family as a social system that provides an important milieu for everyone at certain times in his life.

THE FAMILY

The family has two basic functions: the socialization of the young and the management of tension in adults. Although the latter function can be found elsewhere, no efficient substitute for the first seems to have been discovered even though a considerable literature debating the universality of the family as a socializing institution exists.*

First we shall deal with some persistent myths about the family that do not appear to be true, then we shall discuss some family patterns that have been discovered to be related to length of onset of mental illness, hospitalization, and likelihood to relapse. Finally, we shall suggest ways for using families to expedite ego restitution, and speculate about possible structural equivalents for certain family constellations.

Little of what we know through research into the relationship between the mentally ill and their families has been put to therapeutic use because society places such a high value on family life that we are unwilling to tamper with its operation, even when it does not work well. However, our strong values about the family do not preclude ambivalence. It has been easy to accept the idea of the rejecting, overprotecting mother whose relationship with her child is intimately tied up with the onset of his schizophrenia, even though the evidence of such a uniform behavior pattern is less than completely satisfactory. The other side of our ambivalence shows up when those who accept this idea without question make great efforts to insure that a patient does not lose his family role when he is admitted to a hospital. It is rarely that any thought is given to returning a patient to anything but his own family when that family is willing and able to take him back.

---

* See, for example, numerous selections in the collection of Bell and Vogel.[7]

Unfortunately, we have less information about what goes on in good homes than what happens in bad ones. Most people feel that their own childhood homes were in some way imperfect settings for the socialization of children, and psychiatrists themselves, to hear them talk sometimes, do not always feel certain that they are really filling their children's needs. The ideal home may well exist only as a cultural myth. Divorce, for example, is often said to be breaking up homes and causing malignant environments for children, but never has a larger proportion of the population been married, and, moreover, a minority of divorces occur during the period of socialization of children. If they do occur, the family is usually soon reconstituted through remarriage. It is relatively rare, outside of certain subcultural groups, to find a child being socialized in a family in which both parents, or surrogates, are not present. There is no real basis for thinking that family life has collapsed.

It probably was our mixed ideas about the virtues of family life that led us, in some places, to develop "family care" programs for the mentally ill. Patients were thought of as being happier in private homes than they would be in hospitals, just as children were thought of as being happier in foster homes than they would be in orphanages.* Patients assigned to family care have usually been stable, desocialized, chronic patients. Implicit in the assignment has been the assumption that the patients were not going to improve. In spite of this, they often have improved somewhat. In view of the fact that the families providing care are not usually taught how to structure the milieu, the improvement of the patients assigned to them speaks

---

* The cases are dissimilar. It seems clear that a child must interact with a full complement of normatively grounded adult role holders for socialization to be complete. It is not clear that this is always necessary for ego repair in adults.

more for the poverty of the hospital than for the excellence of the family as a therapeutic instrument.

Malzberg (see *Social and Biological Aspects of Mental Disease*) in one of the more vigorous inquiries into the association of various forms of family life with mental illness, showed that the proportion of married men admitted to mental hospitals was smaller than the proportion of single men so admitted; whereas the proportion of married women was greater than that of single women. However, widowed or divorced women were more disadvantaged than men. Malzberg attributes the higher rate of admission among single men than among married men to the same cause as the failure of these single men to marry: he thinks it is because they are already inadequate owing to their illness. We have noted previously (in Chapter 4) a group of male schizophrenics discovered in our own researches who were mainly unmarried, whose illnesses had persisted for many years before hospitalization, and who were occupationally inadequate (see Cumming and Miller, "Isolation, Family Structure and Schizophrenia"). Most of these men were dependent on parents or older siblings. Since they had never worked effectively, there seemed to be little expectation that they would ever do so. Those men who had the longest elapsed time between the onset of their illness and their hospitalization were very frequently found to have a sister who was within five years of their own age. It is possible that these sisters were playing a typical socio-emotional role and were thereby neutralizing some of the tension arising from the presence of a dependent adult child within the family. George Brown [8] and Morris Carstairs have shown that a group of rehabilitated chronic schizophrenics had a better prognosis if they went to the homes of siblings or to lodging houses than if they returned to their wives or mothers. Howard Freeman and Ozzie Simmons [9] showed that returning to the parental

home was associated with a poor social adjustment.* Similarly,
our tentative findings seem to indicate [10] that discharged patients who have regular visiting patterns with sisters, aunts, or
nieces are less likely to feel stigma from their hospital stay
than those who visit with mothers, who visit with male kin
only, or do not visit at all. There is increasing evidence that
the sibling type of bond, characterized by sociability without
intense obligation, is of benefit to those who have been psychotic, and especially to those who have been schizophrenic.

We have mentioned before that those who have never
worked seem to be able to keep a role in their family of orientation. However, among married men who, for a period at
least, have been occupationally adequate, stopping work often
precipitates hospitalization, even though symptoms may be
objectively no more prominent than they were formerly. Not
being able to work is not in itself a symptom of mental illness,
but in this society more deviance seems to be overlooked if a
man can perform adequately in his central work role.

In many cases where there has been a long history of instrumental inadequacy, hospitalization results not from any
dramatic change in symptoms but from the fact that the family
itself changes through time. For the single man, parents become
older, retire, and eventually die. Siblings marry and leave home,
and with these changes the family loses its holding power—that
is, its ability to absorb and contain deviance. A married woman
who is inadequate may continue to be supported by her husband for long periods, but this task may increase with the birth
of each child—especially if she has no relatives to help her.
Hospitalization for such a woman may depend, for example,
on the spacing between the second and third child or upon the

---

* This does not seem to be true for those who had suffered from affective psychosis. They seemed actually to benefit from the obligatory
and affective relationships which schizophrenics find impossible to live
with.

death of her mother who has done her housework for years. For many inadequate women there seems to be a "last straw": the ego dedifferentiation that accompanies adding new people to the highly cathected group is always a minor crisis, but when there are heavy role demands, and no outside support, it may lead to total disorganization or the exacerbation of underlying ego deficits.

Although the family is one of the major supports that can prevent hospitalization, it may also contribute to tensions that show themselves in symptoms. In addition, when the family decides that further control of a deviant member is needed, they seek it in certain orderly ways. Inferences can be made from our own work [11] that those family members with a diffuse obligatory bond to the patient—such as spouses or parents—first attempt to control his deviance. When they fail, there is a period when kin with sociable ties—such as siblings, and especially sisters—attempt to support him. If this fails, it is those who are responsible for the patient who urge him into the hands of the physician or the priest, and ultimately into the hospital.

This pattern of sociable kin giving support while responsible kin exercise control of the deviant tends to confirm our finding that sisters and sister-surrogates are vital to the maintenance of the *status quo*.

We have noted that patients who go from their families to the hospital usually return to their families at discharge. When hospitalization has resulted from the aging of the family, the family no longer has the power to give the patient the support that he needs, nor the ingenuity to place him in situations where he might become more competent. Freeman and Simmons (in "Mental Patients in the Community: Family Settings and Performance Levels") have commented that some discharged patients live on "one-man chronic wards." In such situations, the family will need training in order to support the ex-patient at an adequate level of ego organization.

In the light of the things we know about the abilities of
families to contain psychotic members, it is possible to propose
certain ameliorative actions—that is, to use some members or
members-surrogate of the family as the therapist's agents.

First, it is possible to capitalize on what we know of the
role of sisters and other female relatives in the control of
deviance. However, let us digress to discuss these female kin
in a little more detail. They can be thought of as differing from
mothers and wives in important ways. Spouse and parent-child
bonds involve the patient in the complicated system of communication and reciprocal action that must go on between
people playing complementary roles. For example, work must
be divided into "men's work" and "women's work"—often a
subtle distinction requiring well differentiated cognitive sets.
In contrast, the sibling bond is essentially the solidarity of
people of similar history, goals, and background. To use the
same example, if the siblings are of the same sex work can be
allocated on rational or expedient bases; if they are not, as
the relationship is not defined in terms of sex-role appropriate
behavior, its integrity does not depend upon specialization
being maintained. In a similar way the parent-child relationship requires an articulation of superordinate-subordinate role
expectations that the sibling relationship does not. This means
that in the sibling relationship or one that is defined as essentially egalitarian and redundant—in the sense that no particular
division of labor is expected—there are fewer opportunities for
misunderstanding and failure, less intense involvement and,
hence, affect, and more freedom for the expression of the
tension-reducing aspects of the socio-emotional role.

In the study cited previously in which patients who have
sisters and more distant female relatives available are less liable
to feel stigmatized by hospitalization, we concluded that such
women are able to help the patient formulate a reason for
hospitalization—overwork, nervous exhaustion—that restores

his self-esteem. In one sense these women are like the ward staff: they are committed to the patient's welfare but are not over-involved with him. This may be the underlying reason for their success in playing the socio-emotional role.

How then can we use this information? We could advise certain changes of family structure to include a sister or more distant female relative, but this is seldom practical. We can send a public health nurse as a regular visitor to the household, especially if she has had some training in the care of the mental hospital patient. If she visits twice a week she might be able to solve many of the practical problems that are so often the bane of the families of the mentally ill, and also to lower the tension generated by the hospitalization, thus freeing the patient from the anxiety that keeps him from using his ego resources. She then assumes a role that may have the same end result as the sister's.

Certain other strategies are possible. Brown and Carstairs have shown that if the mothers of male schizophrenics work, the son has a better chance of staying out of the hospital. Such mothers might well be encouraged to work and leave the patient to solve certain structured problems on his own—perhaps with the help of a "philosopher, guide and friend" from the hospital.

In general, there seems reason to believe that depressed people, and possibly alcoholics—who do better on wards where they must care for others—and even some schizophrenics are better if they have someone who looks to *them* for support and help. Acting on the theoretical proposition that both seeing themselves mirrored as competent people and strengthening and differentiating ego organizations through use are good for an ego-damaged person, it might be useful to introduce into the homes of certain depressive women, someone who requires care—for example, an old aunt, a new immigrant, or a foreign student.

There is a wide range of role shifts possible, and there is

also the possibility of temporary dissolutions of the family structure, so that vicious circles causing persistent diffusion feeling can be broken up. This may be especially helpful for the ego disorganization and poor differentiation that we call "paranoid," but this is speculation.

Finally, it should be possible to use substitute family structures for some purposes. For example, young schizophrenics, who require a large interactional input and who cannot, because of their temperaments, generate it for themselves, might be matched and placed in one another's families.

We shall digress briefly to develop this point a little more fully. As we have stated above, there is no compelling evidence for the existence of an innately "schizophrenogenic mother" and there is some evidence [12, 13, 14] that certain patterns of interaction and certain role relationships will result in the condition known as "schizophrenia." Some of these relationships are characterized by an inability of the patient to act and an over-willingness of the mother to act on his behalf. Yet the historical genesis of such situations is not clear; it is sometimes said that the mother is meeting her own needs in dominating the child. However, when we consider that it is in the nature of social life that we come to want to do what we have to do, it seems plausible to imagine that mothers of certain selector-temperament children have been disappointed in their aspirations for them and have somehow translated this disappointment into satisfaction with a perennial mother role. When we see mothers who derive great pleasure from caring for dependent defective children, it seems reasonable to assume that this is a matter of "making the best of a bad job." At any rate, such mothers cannot be called "defecto-genic," and as the mothers of schizophrenics often resemble these women in their attitudes toward their children, it seems reasonable to imagine that their behavior has been learned and has, over time, developed a vicious-circle quality. Their behavior then produces malignant results when outside efforts to help the patient toward independence meet their learned patterns of making his decisions for him.

However, it is possible to relearn, and our proposal for an exchange of matched schizophrenics is based on this possibility. The patients must first have been treated in a therapeutic milieu so that they have had opportunities to see themselves mirrored back in "normal" role relationships. For this reason it might be advisable to retrain the mother by putting a normal person of the patient's age into the home. Perhaps a college student would be willing to try this role in exchange for board and lodging. If the mother could learn to interact with this surrogate, she might, with careful instruction about how to *behave,* take a substitute schizophrenic. If the mother is taught to behave in somewhat the way aides and nurses do, and is told why it is important, she may learn to take satisfaction in seeing the patient succeed. Whether or not this retraining would ever carry over to the mother's own child would depend on a balance between the redintegration of historical attitudes and affects and the potency of the new pattern. At any rate, such an experiment could throw important light on some of our problems in the social rehabilitation of schizophrenics and on the plasticity of family interaction patterns.

We shall return now to a discussion of other community milieus.

OTHER ENVIRONMENTS

We have stated before that both the school and the job are pervasive, influential milieus in which ego-restorative forces can be expected to be ubiquitous. We say this because we assume that any society organizes itself in ways that tend to control individual deviance and generate enough satisfactions to stabilize ego structure. It is therefore unlikely that any

major institution will be ego-damaging as such. It may assume
values that we detest, as in the Nazi school systems, or that
we deplore, as in the "soft" schools, but it does not, *for this
reason,* injure ego organization or structure. Therefore we assume that only rarely do vicious circles of ego-damaging interaction arise in society's major institutions. In fact, schools, with
their graded series of problems, are the prototype of growth-
inducing institutions.

Neither the school nor the factory has been examined
specifically in terms of forces that make for ego repair, and
therefore we have no hard ground of fact to stand on. We shall,
instead, turn our attention to some other community environments about which we know more and about which we thus
can tentatively prescribe action.

We shall begin by discussing briefly the distribution of
ego-damaged people in a community. A recent study of our
own carried out in an industrial city [15] showed that there are
"pools" of "seriously disturbed" people in the public welfare
department, the free public health services—including public
health nursing agencies—the shelters, the probation department, and the police station. When the workers in these environments were interviewed about these people, they complained that they did not have staff members trained to help
them and that they desperately needed other resources. Our
study further showed that agencies with highly trained workers
did not encounter the more seriously ego-damaged patients.
This was because of policy and because the workers believed
that their skills were more gainfully employed with less impaired people, but it was also because these workers did not
want to take the responsibility for maintaining control of these
patients outside a hospital. The psychiatric clinics and the
family service agencies, with the most highly trained staff of all,
were found to resist the efforts of the other agencies to get
service for these people and to complain that it was hard to

train the community agencies to "make good referrals." * Examining this overdetermined problem further, it looks as if highly trained workers have skills for dyadic therapies only, and as if they evaluate therapies of this kind—particularly if they involve insight—higher than giving advice or concrete help.

There does not seem to be any reason to believe that these highly trained people will soon undertake to treat seriously ego-damaged people, because the dyadic verbal therapies that are the primary skill of these professionals do not seem to work well on ego-damaged people. It seems evident that treatment for these people will have to be given in the environments to which they filter, and by those who already work with them. This does not mean that these workers should be given psychiatric training, however, because this equips them to give dyadic verbal treatment with the result that they join an agency that does not treat the seriously ego-damaged patient.

We shall now make a few suggestions about the roles of welfare departments, police, and public shelters and say a few words about the special case of the general hospital.

Any service that reduces physical or social disorganization helps to maintain ego function, as we pointed out in Chapter 5. Thus, homemaking service to overworked mothers can help just by restoring physical order. The police already perform a supportive function for ego-damaged people. Researches of our own show that much of a policeman's routine activity is concerned with clarifying ambiguities and restoring temporarily disorganized situations to the *status quo ante*. Policemen say

---

* One is reminded ironically of Frank's description of the shamans who, ". . . usually are adept at distinguishing illnesses they can treat successfully from those that are beyond their powers, and they manage by one means or another to reject patients with whom they are likely to fail. This enables them to maintain a reputation for success which, by arousing favorable expectancies in the patient and the group, undoubtedly enhances their healing power." [16]

that they only act to prevent the law from being broken, and whether or not this is true is impossible to tell. If, for example, they are called to a house in a slum area where a family fight is in progress, they are able to describe clearly the protection that the law offers to the various people involved, point out the consequences of their actions, and in many cases, apparently through their symbolic role as keeper of the norms, restore equilibrium.

Recalling that the police in Kansas City felt that they had learned a lot from their training in the hospital, we can guess that it would be reasonable to train policemen in simple techniques for calming disturbed people. However, police are basically controlling agents and should not be put into conflict by being asked to act also as supportive ones. Their job of control could be easier if they had a little more skill in providing temporary structure in chaotic situations. On the telephone, in the station, and from the prowl car, police already give out to citizens an enormous flow of cognitive, orientating information about the expectations of society and the sanctions that will follow certain acts. For people in severe doubt about the nature of reality—in our terms, with temporarily dedifferentiated sets and a certain amount of ego disorganization— such information might make all the difference between acute disorganization and a return to equilibrium.

We have dwelled on the positive contributions of the police; there are cases where they inflict ego insults, especially when citizens have violated their strongly held norms, but in general they appear, from our studies, to contribute considerable structure to the types of environments in which numbers of seriously disordered people find themselves.

Departments of public welfare have a constant clientele of inadequate people, many of whose ego organizations are neither complex nor various enough for independent living. Welfare departments, on the whole, stigmatize recipients and are oriented to making sure that assistance is not undeservedly received. Because of this, applicants must give evidence of being without means, and without an ability of getting means, before they can be helped. For people in precarious states of ego organization, the proof of need is the proof of inadequacy. Furthermore, for people of adequate ego structure caught in an economic slump, this process can be, as we know from many studies, undermining.* It must be remembered that the stigma attached to helplessness is fundamentally related to society's inability to tolerate too much deviant behavior. Economic inadequacy is particularly stigmatized in this society, probably because of our materialistic emphasis. We cannot expect society's agents to welcome dependency, but enlightened self-interest alone would suggest that ego-damaged people be removed to situations that resemble the work program described in Chapter 11. This is, of course, a matter for legislation, but there seems very little doubt that our method of handling inadequacy to a large degree defeats its own purpose, and the pool of ego-damaged people in the community is increased rather than diminished by these methods.

There are agencies in all communities that give support and advice to a large group of people who have marginal ego adjustments. These are the public health nursing agencies, the medical agencies, shelters, and family services of some welfare departments and of some religious groups. These workers could probably be taught more skills for helping their clients to solve their problems, and, indeed, we know that many of them would welcome such additional training. We ourselves have given intensive academic and field training [17] to a group of public

---

* Attempts to set up special intensive treatment units for a special few welfare clients point up the conflict in the professional worker's mind over who should receive the service they are trained to give. It is interesting, too, that this type of special service, by picking out a select group, further stigmatizes the remainder.

health nursing supervisors and their staff nurses to prepare
them to work with patients released from state mental hospitals.
There does not seem to be any real reason to suppose that most
people who work with ego-damaged groups cannot be trained
to a much higher pitch of usefulness without giving them the
kinds of skills that make them eager to handle the more hopeful
and better-integrated patients.

Finally, we shall say something about the hospitalization
crisis of physically ill people. Because the hospital is the stuff of
their everyday lives, general hospital personnel can easily forget
that most people find hospitalization a difficult experience that
challenges their assumptive states, occasionally to the point of
disorganization. There are certain ways in which hospitalization
can be handled in order to minimize its undermining effects.
To return to an old theme, we often forget how continuously
we rely upon others' responses for reassurance about our identity
—especially in crises. Some hospitals, during periods of staff
shortage, have adopted the so-called "functional nursing." In
such hospitals, aides and assistants are trained to perform such
specific functions as taking temperatures, giving baths, or
distributing ice water. An aide who has been taught to take
temperatures will take all the temperatures, another aide will
take fresh ice water to each patient, a third will distribute news-
papers and mail, and so on. Following the same pattern, a
graduate nurse will give the medication, but she, too, will go
around the ward to all the patients and perhaps make only
this one contact with patients. Nurses in this scheme are not
nursing patients but, rather, performing functions. After several
days of being treated in this way, a patient can develop a feeling of unreality that may not be counteracted by interactions
with visitors from outside. In such situations, an aide's preoccupation with some specific function such as temperature taking coupled with her lack of training in bedside skills can create
the impression that she is bored by her patient or indifferent to

him. The aide, however, may feel awkward in any but the temperature-taking role. After a few days a patient can get the uncomfortable feeling that he is only an adjunct to the thermometer; he does not have an acceptable identity mirrored back to him and diffusion feelings followed by depression or depersonalization may set in. Only if a patient is not very ill and is of robust temperament can he interrupt an aide's routine long enough to tell her, and hence himself, who he is and what he is doing there.

Sometimes, under such a system, mistakes can further undermine the ego. For example, the food trays get into the wrong rooms because the aide who takes them around is not quite certain of the patients' names and the numbers are written unclearly. The patient, seeing someone else's name on his tray, may well wonder whether anyone in the hospital knows who he is, whether his doctor reads the proper chart, whether anyone is concerned with his welfare, or whether, as it seems, the hospital simply exists to get a series of fragmented tasks accomplished.

We have spoken of the general hospital because, although it is a structured milieu, it serves large numbers of patients from many kinds of backgrounds and is sensitive to community pressure. Our own interest is directed toward an understanding of how to change ego-undermining to ego-integrative forces without major changes of resources. There is, of course, a great amount of literature about general nursing and the reader is referred especially to the work of Orlando (see *The Dynamic Nurse-Patient Relationship*) and that of Esther Brown.[18]

This chapter has been wide ranging and disperse because our knowledge of the therapeutic potential of natural milieus is fragmentary and our skills almost totally unvalidated. In the concluding chapter, we shall try to tie up some theoretical and practical loose ends.

References

[1] R. E. L. FARIS and H. W. DUNHAM, *Mental Disorders in Urban Areas: An Ecological Study of Schizophrenia and Other Psychoses* (Chicago: University of Chicago Press, 1939).

[2] AUGUST B. HOLLINGSHEAD and FREDRICK C. REDLICH, *Social Class and Mental Illness* (New York: John Wiley & Sons, 1958).

[3] BENJAMIN MALZBERG, *Social and Biological Aspects of Mental Disease* (Utica, N. Y.: State Hospitals Press, 1940).

[4] M. L. KOHN and J. A. CLAUSEN, "Parental Authority Behavior and Schizophrenia," *American Journal of Orthopsychiatry*, 26 (April 1956), 297-313.

[5] E. H. HARE, "Family Setting and the Urban Distribution of Schizophrenia," *Journal of Mental Science*, 102 (October 1956), 753-760.

[6] LIONEL COSIN, in a speech to the Blue Cross–Blue Shield groups, Kansas City, Mo., 1957.

[7] NORMAN BELL and EZRA VOGEL (eds.), *The Family* (Glencoe, Ill.: Free Press, 1960).

[8] GEORGE W. BROWN, "Experiences of Discharged Chronic

Schizophrenic Patients in Various Types of Living Group," *Milbank Memorial Fund Quarterly*, XXXVII, 2 (1959), 105.

[9] HOWARD E. FREEMAN and OZZIE G. SIMMONS, "Mental Patients in the Community: Family Settings and Performance Levels," *American Sociological Review*, 23 (April 1958), 147-154.

[10] ELAINE CUMMING, JOHN CUMMING, and RHONDDA K. CASSETTA, "The Social Psychology of Stigma" (paper read to the Annual Meetings of the American Sociological Association, Washington, D.C., August 28, 1962).

[11] ELAINE CUMMING, "Phase Movement in the Support and Control of Psychiatric Patients" (paper read to the Eastern Sociological Society, Philadelphia, April 7, 1962).

[12] GREGORY BATESON and others, "Toward a Theory of Schizophrenia," *Behavioral Science*, 1 (October 1956), 251-264.

[13] MURRAY BOWEN, "Family Relationships in Schizophrenia," in Alfred Auerback (ed.), *Schizophrenia—An Integrated Approach* (New York: Ronald Press, 1959).

[14] LYMAN C. WYNNE and others, "Pseudo-Mutuality in the Family Relations of Schizophrenics," *Psychiatry*, 21 (May 1958), 205-220.

[15] CLAIRE RUDOLPH and JOHN CUMMING, "Where Are Additional Psychiatric Services Most Needed?" (*Social Work*, June, 1962).

[16] JEROME D. FRANK, *Healing and Persuasion* (Baltimore: Johns Hopkins Press, 1960).

[17] JOHN CUMMING, N. BIGELOW, A. HALPERN, C. CALTHROP, and M. CRILL, "The Public Health Nurse and After-care," Supplement 2, *Psychiatric Quarterly* (1961).

[18] ESTHER L. BROWN, *Newer Dimensions in Patient Care* (New York: Russell Sage Foundation, 1961).

CHAPTER 13

Loose Ends

In this final chapter we shall try to tie up some loose ends and open up some new issues by noting ambiguous areas, by discussing some ethical points concerning the practice of milieu therapy, and by giving some indication of where the theory seems to have its major usefulness.

THEORY

It seems obvious that our theory rests upon a concept of the nature of man which is somewhat different from that underlying the theories of the insight therapies. In general, the latter seem to assume that the valued man is, in many ways, a hidden thing to be revealed only under propitious circumstances —and perhaps never. Perhaps it is the same set of assumptions that leads to the belief that there are "mute inglorious Miltons" among us. These are theories of the secret side of man, and it is interesting that they were developed in an atmosphere of interest in and concern for the inner anguish of patients.

Our theory is based on an assumption that the valued man *is* his act, and that there is a continuity between the inner and the outer man such that every time he acts he acts in his entirety. This may be a result of our concern with disorders grave enough to stifle rational and social action, and our concern with providing the basic minima of social survival. It may be possible to combine these assumptions so as to reach a stronger theoretical position. At any rate, it is obvious that there are many assumptions that can be made about essential man, and ours is only one of them.

Our theory is in some ways a traditional biosocial theory embracing assumed neurophysiological substrata, congenital temperament, emerging biological stages, developmental crises, and the interactional aspects of personality. For schizophrenia, this seems roughly satisfactory, although we have not dealt with the issue of whether or not milieu therapy is thought of as *curing* schizophrenia. At this stage, it is not. Rather, it is thought of as arming the schizophrenic with skills that make his deficits less catastrophic. We do not feel, for example, that milieu therapy can alter an extreme reactor temperament in a patient, but it may provide him with instrumental and social skills sufficient to render his basic temperament less painful to himself and to others.

On the whole we must remember that our knowledge of severe schizophrenia has been limited to its course in a hospital, and prognoses have been based on the ability of a patient to remain outside. We have no real knowledge of the extent or distribution of the "one-man chronic wards" that Freeman and Simmons have described. Until we have tried to treat this great ego disorder outside hospitals and have turned our best efforts to caring for it in more normal social contexts, we cannot come to any firm conclusions about its curability.

It is assumed throughout this book that the synthetic and executive functions of the ego are inseparable and that change in one function affects both. Nevertheless, we have developed the theory almost exclusively in executive function terms, and in this sense it lacks symmetry. In general, the theory is most powerful in accounting for ego damage that clearly affects instrumental function. The theory is least complete where damage can be most economically described in synthetic function terms. Therefore, though the ego is viewed holistically, it is obviously not so in any simple sense, and this is an open area in the theory.

Finally, we have said nothing about insight, and this is a reflection of the pragmatic origins of the theory. Insight, however, can be thought of in two ways: it is either a goal, or it is a means. As a goal, it is subsumed under the absolute value that knowledge—more particularly knowledge of man—is good. If, with Fromm,[1] we agree that man is at his best when he is most human, then he will be at his best when he is best attuned to himself. But problems arise. The Socratic "know thyself" was not an exhortation to self analysis as such but rather to "know thyself in order to know mankind." Can mankind not be known as well by reading Dostoevski? Is seeing clearly inward sometimes so beguiling that it detracts from the gift of seeing outward? These problems spring up around the question of whether or not insight is in itself good.

The more important question, from the point of view of this book, is the efficacy of insight. There may be a range of disorders for which short-term, symptom-directed, psychoanalytically oriented therapy will always be the most effective treatment. However, it may be possible to develop refined combinations of the two therapies that surpass either of them.

THE PROBLEMS OF EVALUATION

Appraisal of milieu therapy has scarcely begun, but it can benefit from the problems that have confounded attempts to appraise the individual therapies. It is curious that although psychotherapists seem universally enthusiastic about their clinical successes, no evaluation seems to bear them out. As

Alexander Astin [2] has pointed out, hope for proof of efficacy, high in the early days of psychotherapy, faded when the results of appraisals started to come in. Finally, many therapists, apparently as clinically optimistic as ever, retreated to a safer position and declared psychotherapy to be its own justification. Many other therapists, among them members of the research section of the Group for the Advancement of Psychiatry,[3] believe that the failure to demonstrate the gains made in psychotherapy lies with the type of study undertaken. They contend that we do not yet know how to appraise the results of psychiatric treatment.

Milieu therapy shares with individual therapy the latter's "unproven" status. However, the former's problems are a little different. Whereas psychotherapy sets out to make "basic"— that is, intrapsychic—changes, usually expecting social improvement to follow, milieu therapy sets out to make social changes and trusts that ego growth will ensue. For this reason, it is easier for milieu therapists to evaluate their proximal product. Accounts such as those of Barnes, Freudenberg and Bennett, Brooks, and particularly Wing and Brown, in the works cited in this book, are a big step in this direction. Another type of evaluation based on measurements of personal and social attributes is being undertaken by Richard Sanders [4] and others. However, two serious problems remain, of which the first is easier to solve than the second. The first problem is that the terms "milieu therapy" or "therapeutic community" as generally used mean nothing. Because Jones has an inventor's claim to the latter term, it sometimes refers specifically to his rather highly specialized technique, but otherwise labels seem only to mean something vaguely benign in intent. Often, as we have pointed out in the introduction, they refer simply to the addition of one hour of group therapy a day or perhaps the addition of patient government. It is interesting, too, that many of those who have developed successful rehabilitation programs are as reluctant to describe the day-by-day process as the psychotherapists are to submit to observation. It is therefore important to develop a standard way of discussing the milieu—perhaps in terms of such things as hours of structured activity, content of ward program, and allocation of decision-making authority.

The second, and more difficult, problem of evaluation is the estimation of ego growth resulting from the therapeutic milieu. It is our clinical belief that such growth occurs, but we are sobered by the continuing faith of the psychotherapists in the face of negative evidence. However, until an attempt is made, we shall not know the power of our theory.

ETHICAL CONSIDERATIONS

From time to time milieu therapy is termed "brainwashing," and, therefore, it is relevant to distinguish here between these two techniques. They have one important element in common: the use of group theory to achieve an effect. The important difference between them is that brainwashing rests on the belief that means are justified by ends, whereas milieu therapy assumes that means *determine* ends. Every maneuver used in a milieu program should be able to stand upon its own feet as a reasonable therapeutic act, doing no harm and, hopefully, doing good. The goal of treatment is to allow a patient to return to society able to conform if he chooses.

Not far under this discussion lies the question of values. It has been argued by those favoring dyadic therapies that milieu treatments merely use a patient's vulnerability to change his value system. There is truth in this, and we have discussed this fairly fully in Chapter 8. However, it is our belief that every time people interact, or fail to do so, somebody's values will be modified; that is the nature of social life. When the actors are on equal terms, in the sense of having equal control of information and equal status and power, the process of change may be reciprocal; when they are not, as when adults interact with children or well people with sick people, the change tends to be more markedly in one direction. However, we see no reason to believe that a two-person relationship, in which one member is intensely involved with another because the latter is a symbol of past relationships, is any more immune from this value-creating, value-changing process than a group relationship is. Evidence, of course, would be most welcome—one way or the other.*

In the end, the moral and ethical problems surrounding the use of any therapy seem to be inexorably tied to the medical ethic. There may be shades of difference in the ideal "well man" in the minds of different kinds of therapists—that is, some may strive for autonomy sufficient for participation and others for participation sufficient for autonomy—but in the end both are bound by the ethic that says that it is toward the patient's welfare that all these efforts are directed. The problem of determining *whose concept of his welfare should be used* is endemic in the healing and helping arts. As moral and ethical beings, these are the problems we face and must solve as best we can. Our own position, we hope, has been made clear in this book. In essence, we see the goal of therapy as enabling the patient to be, as far as he is able, free to act in accordance with ideas and values he has chosen to conform to.

We turn finally to the practical aspects of this theory and make two points—one specific and one general. Specifically, we take no cognizance in this book of the problem of the ego state of the ward staff member or the milieu therapist. It is interesting that the specifications for ego growth—the solution of many problems in a protected situation—suggest that the ward staff of a successful program will develop immensely strong egos.

---

* Jerome Frank in *Healing and Persuasion* proposes that the psychotherapist trains the patient to his point of view in a process of operant conditioning.

It would be interesting to know if they do. Perhaps, if the ward staff could be compared on several indexes with employees of similar rank in noninteractive occupations, we would know more than we do now about the validity of this theory and, fortuitously, more about personnel selection.

From the practical point of view, the most important matter is the relationship of milieu treatment to the logistics of treating the total population of the mentally ill. As we have observed in Chapter 12, our own researches have shown that the more psychiatric education any group of people receive, the more they will limit their attention to the least ill. The Joint Commission's report on manpower trends [5] gives an explanation of why this is so. The techniques of teaching, and the conditions under which psychiatry is taught, lead inevitably to private and limited practice. The Commission's manpower report is itself a lucid statement of this problem of the increasing gap between a mildly impaired group receiving a great deal of service and a seriously impaired group receiving a minimum. There is no reason to believe that this situation will be ameliorated in the measurable future as the centers of training are largely organized and run by practitioners oriented to one-to-one therapy in a private situation.

It is possible that a resolution might come from the transfer of a considerable body of psychiatric practice to the field of public health. There is no doubt that there will never be enough practitioners to treat all of the mentally ill one at a time because of the length and social cost of the training period. Nor does the model of individual medicine apply uniformly to the practice of psychiatric medicine. Its major problems are organization of care, techniques for treating large groups of people, and rehabilitation. In addition, a public health orientation seems suitable to the control of illnesses that are basically social in their definition and consequences.

We are convinced that this or some other theory based on social interaction is essential for understanding and conquering the great illnesses still beyond our control. In the end, as Kurt Lewin said, there is nothing so practical as a good theory.

References

[1] ERICH FROMM, *Man For Himself*—An Inquiry into the Psychology of Ethics (New York: Rinehart, 1947).

[2] ALEXANDER W. ASTIN, "The Functional Autonomy of Psychotherapy," *American Psychologist,* 16 (February 1961), 75-78.

[3] *Some Observations on Controls in Psychiatric Research,* Report No. 42 (New York: Group for the Advancement of Psychiatry, May 1959).

[4] RICHARD SANDERS and others, "Social Treatment of the Male Chronic Mental Patient" (paper read to the Annual Meeting of the American Psychological Association, New York, 1961).

[5] GEORGE W. ALBEE, *Mental Health Manpower Trends* (New York: Basic Books, 1959).

INDEXES

Subject Index

279

Name Index